2.69.

The Com

Deborah Bosley was born in South London in 1965. She is the author of the *Rough Guide to San Francisco* and a reviewer for the *Literary Review*. Her first novel *Let Me Count The Ways* was published in 1996 to huge critical acclaim and was shortlisted for the Romantic Novelists Association Award. This is her second novel.

This book is dedicated to my family

The Common Touch

Deborah Bosley

ARROW

This edition published by Arrow Books Limited 1999

1 3 5 7 9 10 8 6 4 2

Copyright c 1999 Deborah Bosley

All rights reserved

Deborah Bosley has asserted her right under the Copyright, Designs
and Patents Act, 1988, to be identified as the author of this work

This book is sold subject to the condition that it shall not, by way of trade or otherwise, be lent,
resold, hired out, or otherwise circulated without the publisher's prior consent in any form of
binding or cover other than that in which it is published and without a similar condition
including this condition being imposed on the subsequent purchaser.

First published in the United Kingdom in 1998 by Century,
Random House UK Ltd, 20 Vauxhall Bridge Road, London SW1V 2SA

Arrow Books Ltd
Random House UK Ltd, 20 Vauxhall Bridge Road, London SW1V 2SA

Random House Australia (Pty) Limited
20 Alfred Street, Milsons Point, Sydney,
New South Wales 2061, Australia

Random House New Zealand Limited
18 Poland Road, Glenfield
Auckland 10, New Zealand

Random House South Africa (Pty) Limited
Endulini, 5a Jubilee Road,
Parktown 2193, South Africa

Random House UK Limited Reg No 954009

A CIP catalogue record for this book
is available from the British Library

Papers used by Random House UK Limited are natural, recyclable products made from wood
grown in sustainable forests. The manufacturing processes conform to the
environmental regulations of the country of origin.

ISBN 0 09 979591 4

Printed and bound in Norway by AIT Trondheim AS

CHAPTER ONE

Douggie Gets Excited

'Come on, Rita, get out of that bloody bath.' Douggie Fisher fidgeted outside his en-suite bathroom, dressed and ready, jingling the change in his pockets.

'Oh sod off Douggie, I've been on my feet all day. I haven't had five minutes.'

'We're supposed to be there at half-eight. It's quarter-to already.' He leaned in closer to the door and sniffed. 'I thought you were packing those fags up.'

'I am,' she shouted.

'Oh yeah? I can smell it out here.'

'Oh so what? It's my bathroom.'

Douggie had an answer but thought better of it. Although his wife did him the favour of deferring to him in public, at home she rarely lost an argument. He wandered around the bedroom, looked at his watch then stuffed his hands back in his pockets and stood looking out of the bedroom window at the brown Mercedes in the drive below. He stayed there for about thirty seconds before looking at his watch again: 'Oh for crying out loud.' He slumped on the bed opposite the mirrored wardrobes and studied the pattern of his baldness. He'd tried everything from creative combing to special shampoos. He could be very touchy about his appearance – it was the standing joke in the family: 'Face it, Dad, you're a bald cunt!,' his eldest, Steve, had said when he caught his father reading an advert for a hair transplant clinic in the Sunday paper. 'Less of the bald,' Douggie had replied.

Douggie tutted at his image, then rolled on to his back, lying widthways across the bed. It was enormous. 'Superking – and I don't care if I have to wait while they order one in,' Rita had instructed before dispatching him to Dreams of Croydon on his way to work. Over the years, their beds had grown progressively larger – Douggie tended to thrash around a lot in the night. In front of his wife and children, he affected a couldn't-care-less attitude to life – it was his job to fret about the money and he never brought his problems to the table. But his doubts would come for him in his sleep and he would sweat, roll around and often call out.

'If you can't learn to stay in one place, we're getting separate beds,' Rita would threaten in the mornings.

'We might as well bloody give up now, then.' Douggie felt strongly that single beds were the end of married life.

He stared up at the newly Artexed ceiling and rearranged himself inside his trousers. He usually found touching himself relaxing, but he was anxious about the evening ahead and couldn't settle. He rolled off the bed and went to the bathroom door again. Banging hard he said, 'We're leaving in ten minutes, get a bloody move on.'

Inside the bathroom, Rita assembled her compact ladies' primrose razor; taking it from its little box and screwing the handle into the head – great little razors, really sharp, you didn't see them so much these days. Could take half your leg off if you weren't paying attention. 'What's the matter with you? It's only Frank Skinner. You don't bother to be on time for anyone else.'

'Don't start up about Frank again, Rita, open the poxy door. What are you doing in there?'

'Shaving my legs. That all right with you?'

'Let me in, I want to talk to you.' With one hand on top of the door frame and the other on his hip, he leaned, waiting. He could hear Rita sloshing around and thought she was getting up to open the door. When a few moments had passed and it was still closed he banged again.

'Douggie!' There was a note of warning in his wife's voice.

'What?' he shouted.

'For Christ's sake, go and watch the telly or something.'

Though never a peaceful household, things had been choppier than usual in the Fisher home for about a month. It kicked off in earnest the night Douggie came home late from an impromptu bender with Frank Skinner. He hadn't seen Frank for going on fifteen years the night they bumped into each other at the bar in the Angel on Stockwell Road. At opening time Douggie had closed up his used car lot next door and popped in for his customary two pints while he went through the day's receipts and waited for the rush hour to die down. He'd just sunk the last mouthful of a mild and bitter and motioned his glass at the barman for a refill, when a voice beside him waved a £50 note and said, 'I'll get these.' Douggie turned round to see the dark navy cashmere-coated figure of Frank Skinner, old friend and rival.

When an interval of 'I don't believe it!', 'Well stone me' and 'You're looking fit' had passed, Douggie and Frank settled in at the bar for a long night. Years ago their lives had been closely linked, but Frank had gone on to bigger things and their paths seldom crossed any more. Round about the fifth pint, Frank casually mentioned that he'd recently bought a club in the West End and was looking for a partner. He invited Douggie to come and have a look, bring the wife – hadn't seen Rita for years. After a good bit of back-slapping and shaking of hands they promised to call.

That night, Douggie rolled in at half-eleven, slumped fully clothed on the bed next to his wife and woke her up with the good news. She didn't share his enthusiasm: 'He's two-bob, Douggie, forget it.'

'But baby, he's a millionaire.' Douggie reached under the

covers and stroked her hips and backside. She'd leaned into his touch and softened her voice:

'I don't care, he's still bottom-drawer. And you're pissed. I can't believe you drove home in that state, come to bed.'

It was to be the start of several weeks during which angry voices ricocheted off the walls of their dream home in Purley. When they'd bought it in 1981, it was a shell – no heating, no electric, no nothing. Douggie had worked with his friend John the builder for eight months to get that house up to scratch. Beautiful it was – big, too. Four bedrooms and all the original Victorian fittings. Rita had refused to get carpet until the last drop of paint had been applied and the family had had to endure a long winter hopping about on freezing boards, until the big weekend when the Axminster arrived. The whole house was carpeted in the same honey-coloured soft, short-pile carpet – all except the kitchen which had terracotta tiles on the floor. It was a lovely home and they were happy there. Sort of.

What did he want to go sodding about with a nightclub for anyway? They were doing all right weren't they? The car lot made good money and Rita's flower shop was ticking over. Why did they want to go and stick their savings into a nightclub?

'We're too old, Douggie. Anyway, if Frank's so rich, what does he need your piddling twenty grand for?' Rita had her ideas about Frank and was buggered if she was going to watch Douggie hand over what was left from the sale of the apartment in Fuengirola. She claimed it was all to do with the fall Douggie had taken for Frank. 'Four bloody years you did for him and now you want to give him all our money.' But Douggie didn't hold grudges, and anyway Frank had taken good care of Rita and the kids while he'd been away. He couldn't understand what she was getting so worked up about.

★

That Douggie had persuaded her to come and meet Frank and his wife Doreen at the club for drinks, 'just to have a look', as he put it, was good going. As Rita came down the stairs, Douggie looked approvingly at her black dress and heels. Rita Fisher was ageing well. She made no attempt to look younger than her forty-six years and showed all the signs of three children, but the handsome face still had a glamorous edge. It was more in the way she carried herself – womanly, slow and careful. Her looks were part of the reason Douggie was so concerned about his own appearance. He knew he'd got a good one when he married Rita. 'She'll keep you on your toes that one, she's got class,' his mum Olive had warned him years ago.

Douggie put down his drink and moved across the room towards his wife. 'Look at you all done up to the nines.' He slapped her backside approvingly: 'What are you all tarted up for?'

'Well, it *is* a nightclub. Anyway, Doreen's bound to be in something that cost more than a month's mortgage. Mind my lipstick, Douggie.' Rita kissed him briefly and pulled away. She slipped her cigarettes and lighter into her handbag.

'It's not her fault her old man's loaded. Anyway, it'll be good – you haven't seen her for donkey's years. You used to be good mates, we all did.'

'Yeah well, we'll see. Come on then.' Rita moved into the hall and picked up her beaver lamb fur coat from the banister. The front door opened and their youngest son, Ronnie, walked in, dumping his bag with his football kit on the floor.

'Hello love, how was practice? Don't leave that bag there, put it in your room.'

'Yeah all right Mum, don't start,' he said taking off his coat. Then looking up at her: 'You look nice. How come you're all done up?'

'I'm going out with your father, to see Frank's club.' Rita rolled her eyes at her son. She tried not to have favourites, but she really loved Ronnie. He was no trouble, her baby. Getting big now though, fifteen, taller than his dad and his big brother. Lovely-looking kid too. Douggie came into the hallway whistling.

'Might be *my* club an' all after tonight. What do you reckon then Ron, your old dad owning a nightclub?' Douggie punched his son on the arm.

'I think you're a bit sad actually, Dad.' Ronnie walked into the kitchen. Douggie called after him:

'What do you mean? I can still dance.' He attempted the twist but owing to the ridged sole on his shoe, couldn't slide across the carpet quite as he might have liked. Rita shoved her husband towards the door.

'Come on Douggie, jigging about with the bloody door open, it's freezing. Ronnie, there's some pizza and chips in the freezer for your tea and don't forget to wash up when you've finished. I don't know where your sister is, she went straight out again when she got back from work. Didn't say a word.'

'Good. She gets on my nerves,' Ronnie replied. Rita clicked down the path in her heels, tutting to herself, and Douggie shouted to his son before he closed the door: 'And don't drink any of my beers either. I've counted them.'

Traffic was bad. They spent half an hour just getting past Croydon. 'Christ almighty Rita, look at the time.' Douggie was getting agitated. 'We're not going to get there till about nine now.'

'So, he'll wait.' Rita opened the window and lit a cigarette.

'Do you have to smoke in my car?' Douggie wiped a bit of ash off the dash.

'It's not your car, Doug, you're supposed to be selling it.' Rita exhaled her smoke sideways out of the window.

'Maybe we should buy it.' He cast a furtive glance, to see her reaction.

'I'd rather we bought this than gave Frank Skinner our money.' Rita reached in her bag for peppermints. With one hand on the wheel, Douggie squeezed her thigh. 'Don't worry love, I'm not saying we should definitely do it, but we'd be mad not to have a look. You can make a bomb out of these clubs.'

'How would you know? You haven't been in one since we sold the flat in Spain and anyway, it's different over there.'

Rita chewed on a hangnail, thinking. Rain started falling softly down the windows of the car and inside they fogged up. By the time they reached Streatham it was bucketing down and Rita wished she'd stayed at home with Ronnie. *The Way We Were* was on at nine o'clock and Robert Redford was her favourite. She sighed at the weather: 'We'll have to stick this in a garage, we're not going to be able to park it in Soho.'

'Nah, s'all right. Frank said he'd save us a space outside the club. He's got a load of those police cones.' Douggie chuckled. 'He's a boy, old Frank.'

As promised, four red-and-white striped cones announcing Metropolitan Police guarded a space large enough for two cars in Poland Street just before the junction with Great Marlborough. Douggie rolled down the window and called to two dinner-suited men in a half-lit doorway, 'Oi, mate! Frank Skinner said I could park here, all right?'

'You Douggie?' called a stocky, middle-aged man. His colleague, a tall handsome black man of about thirty, nodded coolly and piled up the cones on top of one another, then disappeared with them down basement steps. Douggie gave the thumbs-up and called out: 'Cheers son.'

Rita climbed out of the car and smoothed down the creases in her dress. The Poland Club didn't look like much from the outside. Squashed between a double-fronted office building and a Malaysian restaurant it was nondescript and dingy. A dim light shone out from behind wooden blinds, almost closed. She raised a sceptical eyebrow, noting the tatty paintwork on the door and window frames. She wished Douggie would get a move on; it was still drizzling a little bit, but he was busy explaining the beauty of a Mercedes engine to the bouncer, who by the way of greeting had said, 'Nice motor.'

They walked into a small wood-panelled reception with deep red carpet and an attractive brunette behind a tall reception desk. Rita looked at the perfectly toned stomach and slender arms poking out of a micro T-shirt and suddenly became aware of how tight her own dress felt. They announced themselves to the brunette who reluctantly interrupted her phone call to lead them through part-glazed double doors into the club proper. It was a room about fifty feet long but only fifteen across. A long stainless-steel bar ran the length of one side and glass tables and velvet-upholstered chairs filled the remaining space. It was no dive. Rita squinted into the darkness looking for a familiar figure. A voice called out behind them, 'Over here, Doug.'

In a recessed corner Frank and Doreen Skinner sat behind a large circular table. They both stood up as Douggie and Rita approached. Rita went first to kiss Doreen and say hello while the men pumped a handshake. 'No kiss for me then, Reet?' asked Frank. For the first time in fourteen years, their eyes locked. Middle age suited him; the skin around the eyes had generously creased but he'd managed to hang on to all his hair and keep himself slim. Rita thought how well the grey hair suited his olive complexion.

'Hello Frank, long time.' She turned slightly, offering her cheek as his mouth came towards hers. He gripped her arm and briefly inhaled her perfume before letting go. There was an awkward moment when nobody wanted to be the first to speak, everyone's eyes darting from one to the other, before Frank took charge.

'Right then, sit down, let's get you a drink.' He motioned to the barman. 'Champagne all right? You always liked bubbles didn't you, Reet.' Rita giggled nervously, careful not to catch his eye while Douggie explained how champagne affected his system – rubbing the groove between his chest muscles he said, 'Gives me terrible heartburn. I'll have a mild and bitter if you don't mind.'

'We don't actually have draught, Doug. I can do you a bottle of lager – Becks, Rolling Rock, Sapporo?'

Douggie looked puzzled and changed his order: 'No, I tell you what, I'll have a Scotch and Coke.' Frank looked at Rita, his mouth twisting into a smile. Suddenly embarrassed by her husband, she wished she'd stayed at home. Turning away from the men, she offered Doreen a Rothmans.

'No thank you Rita, I gave up about four years ago.' Doreen sounded different from how Rita remembered. Posher, somehow. Her face looked a bit strange too. Rita wondered if she was going through the change.

'You still hairdressing?' Rita asked.

'No, I don't work any more. We sold the salon when we moved. Bought a lovely house in Sonning about three years ago, Deanery Gardens.' Doreen turned her face ever so slightly from a plume of Rita's smoke.

'Douggie didn't say you'd left London.' Rita was irked to have this sprung on her. 'Don't think we've ever been to Sonning. No, tell a lie, we went to that restaurant, what's it called, French something, it's on the river, isn't it?'

'The French Horn,' Doreen said.

'Yeah, French Horn, that's it. Douggie couldn't stand it. They made him wear a tie.'

Doreen's face was impassive, like she was wearing a mask or something. After a bit of searching, Rita managed: 'Deanery Gardens sounds nice, is it a cul-de-sac?'

'No. It's the name of the house.'

The barman arrived with the bottle of champagne and

Douggie's Scotch and Coke. After replacing Rita's ashtray he was dismissed, and slipped away. Frank filled three flutes, handed the women their glasses and proposed a toast: 'To old friends and new beginnings.'

The other three repeated, 'Old friends' and clinked glasses.

'Still got the shop then?' Frank asked Rita.

'Yeah, still there. Not much has changed at our end. You seem to be doing all right though.' Rita cast a glance around the club. She noticed there were only a few occupied tables. Nobody looked over thirty.

'It's early yet.' Frank had always been able to tell what she was thinking. 'Doesn't usually get going till about eleven. We get between fifty and eighty in here during the week. It's packed on the weekends, though. Not all kids either. Still, always room for more business. Trouble is, I'm not around enough to really stay on top of it.'

'So what keeps you so busy?' Rita levelled her gaze at Frank.

'The usual. Import, export. What I need is someone here keeping an eye on the place, someone I can trust. I bought it as a going concern and inherited the staff – I know they're all on the fiddle but it's catching them at it that's tricky. I should have a bit more time next year to really concentrate on this place, maybe have a refit, but in the meantime I need someone I can rely on. The only person who isn't going to try and do me is another investor.' Frank winked at Douggie, who winked back, but the pitch was aimed at Rita. 'Ideally I want a partner.'

Rita felt tempted to point out that Douggie didn't have the time to fanny around after him, but decided to let it go. For now. She turned back to Doreen.

'So, how are the kids, Dor?'

'Mark is working for his father and Craig is in Thailand.' Doreen openly studied Rita's face and figure as she spoke, pausing too long for Rita's liking on her midriff straining in her dress.

'Oh, you made that mistake of giving your lot jobs as well. Honestly, these kids, they don't know they're born. Steve's working at the car lot with Douggie and I've got bloody Marilyn in the shop. What's Craig up to in Thailand – travelling?'

'Suppose so, bumming around somewhere.' Doreen didn't seem keen to pursue the line of conversation and diverted: 'It would be lovely for Frank to work with Doug again, someone he can really rely on. That's the trouble when you get to our position, everyone's got an axe to grind.'

'Mmm.' Rita nodded, not really understanding. She studied her old friend. Doreen was thinner than Rita remembered. In terrific shape really, considering she must be pushing fifty. She wore a neat navy blue fitted suit with big shoulders that made her look like she was dressed for a day at the office. Rita wondered whether it was in fashion to look like that. Doreen's hair was still platinum blonde but getting fine from years of colouring. The face was shiny and smooth, but the neck and the hands betrayed her real age. Rita found herself comparing her own work-worn hands to Doreen's manicured ones and was pleased to note that Doreen's had a good many more wrinkles than her own. On her wedding finger sparkled a band of baguette diamonds. Rita couldn't control herself and grabbed Doreen's hand for a closer look. 'Lovely ring, Doreen.'

'It's supposed to be for our silver wedding next year. Tempting fate I suppose but I've been on at him for years to get me an eternity ring.'

'Worth the wait by the looks of it.'

'Yeah. He's not all bad.' Doreen's face relaxed a little. She had always liked Rita; trouble was, Frank did too. It wasn't Rita's fault. She never led him on or anything, but Doreen could always sense *something*.

'For our anniversary last year Douggie bought me a new

11

fridge-freezer. Honestly, he's murder.'

'You soon miss them when they're not around.' Doreen looked pinched as she sipped her champagne and Rita felt a stab of sympathy.

'So what do you do with yourself all day, if you're not working?' she asked.

'Well, I'm going to college three days a week in Reading. I'm doing a History of Art degree.'

'Get away!' Rita was impressed.

'That, and a bit of charity work for children with cancer.'

'Aaahh, that's terrific, Doreen.'

'Well, I've got to keep busy or I'd go mad rattling around in that big house. Sometimes I wish we'd never left London, we had a lot of mates here. Mark lives in Pimlico and Craig's been away for eighteen months. If I didn't go to college the only person I'd speak to would be the cleaner.' Doreen faltered before adding, 'Maybe you could come out one weekend.'

'Well I have to work in the shop on Saturdays, but I'm sure we could sort something out, couldn't we, Douggie?' She poked her husband in the ribs, interrupting him in the middle of a story that involved a lot of arm waving.

'What's that, love?' Douggie turned to his wife.

'Go and see Doreen and Frank's place in Sonning.'

'Yeah, I don't mind. Terrific.' Douggie nodded vigorously and piled a fistful of peanuts into his mouth.

'You should see the gardens, Reet, Doreen's done a lovely job.' Frank held Rita's gaze until she looked away into her bag for a handkerchief she didn't need.

'Well, I didn't design the gardens, that was done by Gertrude Jekyll,' Doreen said. 'I just maintain them.'

'Yeah, with the help of three gardeners,' her husband added unkindly.

Douggie broke his promise to stop at two Scotch and Cokes

and, as usual, Rita had been forced to call for a minicab and arrange for the car to be collected in the morning. Steve would have to pick his father up on the way to work. It had been the same ever since she could remember. Still, she didn't mind, Douggie was a lovely drunk, came over all soppy. She just got maudlin. Much as Rita loved a drink, she harboured a faint distaste for drunk women and Douggie always referred to them as 'slags'. It was best not to chance it.

There was very little traffic as they were driven south through London at 1 a.m. 'See, love. Everything's gonna be all right. We'll have a nice weekend together, Frank and I can look at the numbers, you and Doreen can go shopping or just sod about. It'll be like old times.'

'I'm still not keen, Douggie. Doreen seemed a bit miserable didn't you think?'

'Miserable? Her old man's caked. I'd like to see you fed up in a three-million-pound house.'

'Money isn't everything, Douggie. It's usually just the beginning of trouble; look at all the aggravation we had with that flat in Spain. Best day's work you ever did, getting rid of it.'

'Oh, they're all right, they probably had a row before they came out. Come on love, you saw it in there tonight, it was packed by the time we left. They're doing bloody fortunes over that bar.'

'Doug?'

'Yeah, babe?' Douggie turned towards his wife and placed one arm across the back seat.

'Who's Gertrude Jekyll?'

'How the fuck should I know.'

CHAPTER TWO

A Woman's Work Is Never Done

Wednesdays were Rita's favourite. Not only was it her daughter Marilyn's day off, and therefore about the only day of the week when they wouldn't have an argument, but she closed her flower shop at one o'clock and, if the buses were running on time, she could get from South Croydon to Purley by twenty past.

There had been a time when all the shops in the parade did a half-day on Wednesday, but for the last couple of years only herself and the baker kept the old conventions. All the other shops were owned by Pakistanis now and they were open all the hours God sent. Evenings, Sundays, the lot. To Rita's mind, they worked a lot harder at everything and their kids were always beautifully clean and well turned out. 'Good luck to 'em,' she often said to Douggie when he complained about them taking over all the businesses.

Occasionally she would feel a twinge of guilt when she turned the CLOSED sign around, but consoled herself with the thought that Wednesday afternoons were the only time she could get on with her housework in peace and quiet. Saturday was the busiest day at the shop and she was buggered if she was going to run around with the hoover on a Sunday, the only day of the week the whole family sat down and ate a meal together. Steve would drive over with his girlfriend Shelley from their flat in Norwood and even Marilyn got up in time for Sunday lunch – provided she'd made it back the night before.

She jumped off the bus at the lights in Purley and walked

the quarter of a mile uphill along Foxley Lane to the house. She loved living in Purley and had never regretted getting out of Stockwell. There was a big Sainsbury's at the bottom of the hill, a cinema, loads of shops and plenty of buses into Croydon and beyond. It was big enough to have everything she needed, but once you were off the main drag, away from the busy Brighton Road, the streets were residential, quiet and safe. She didn't have to worry about the kids going out on their own at night and in the five years they'd been living there, the car hadn't been broken into once. It had been Douggie's idea to move further out - 'too many coons' – but now they'd moved, she knew that the drive to Stockwell every day got him down.

She opened the front door and found Flossie in the kitchen with a basket full of shirts. Flossie was Douggie's aunt, a tiny woman with fine purple-tinged hair that she had washed and set every Saturday morning. She'd worked as his reception-ist at the car lot when Douggie first started up. Then when he bought Rita the shop he'd told her, 'You can bloody well give her a job if you're that worried about her, she's driving me up the wall.' So Flossie had worked at Rita's shop for a few years, but when she reached sixty-five, she had to admit she found it tough being on her feet all day. The £15 she now earned for doing the ironing was, according to Douggie, 'money down the bloody drain', but Rita, with her own children almost grown, understood the importance of being needed. Besides, she enjoyed the company.

Douggie had been trying to persuade Rita to get a cleaner for years, but she was adamant that she would not have another woman cleaning her home. Flossie came in twice a week to do the ironing, but that was as far as Rita was pre-pared to let it go. Douggie always complained that Flossie didn't do his shirts properly, but he was, by his own admis-sion, hard to please when it came to a starched collar; one of

Douggie's best jokes and the one he liked to tell at every opportunity was of his favourite sexual fantasy: he opens a wardrobe door and sees thirty perfectly pressed and starched shirts hanging. He comes.

Flossie was struggling with one of Marilyn's bat-sleeved blouses. 'I don't know why you don't make Marilyn do her own ironing. You're too soft on that girl, Rita. When you were her age, you had a kid on the way, a home to run and no Douggie to help you for a while. They don't know they're born these days.'

Flossie slammed the iron down on the edge of the board and a hissing plume of steam rose up. Their conversations always followed the same comforting routine. Doug, the fact that there was never anything good on the telly, and the problem of Marilyn. She went to say something else, but a long hacking cough sent her crumpled jowls quivering. Every time Flossie coughed, Rita prayed that the fags wouldn't get her the same way when she got older.

'The trouble is though, Floss, doesn't matter what I say to her, her dad always lets her off the hook and then I'm made to look like the baddie.' Rita sighed and filled the kettle. 'Cup of tea?'

'Yeah, lovely. I think I will sit down for a minute.' Flossie reached into her pinny pocket and pulled out a pack of Players. 'I've cut down to about twenty a day now.'

'You shouldn't smoke those untipped fags. You should switch to low-tar, Floss.' Rita offered her one of her own.

'They're no good. Like smoking fresh air: you have to suck so hard on the things, you almost pass out.' The cigarette seemed to settle Flossie's breathing and she slurped noisily on the hot tea which Rita placed before her in a bone china cup and saucer. Flossie didn't approve of mugs. 'Well, if she was mine, I'd tell her to sling her hook, little mare.

You're just going to have to put your foot down, it's about time she got a place of her own. Then she can live how she likes, but, while she's under your roof, she should abide by your rules. You'll have to have a word with Douggie.'

'Well, one thing at a time, eh? At the moment I'm trying to persuade him not to go in with Frank Skinner on this nightclub he's got.' Rita looked nervously at Flossie as she said the name.

'Frank Skinner! When did he turn up again?' Flossie settled her cup noisily on its saucer.

'Couple of weeks ago. Douggie bumped into him in the Angel. Came home totally lagered and said he wanted to give Frank all our money from the apartment. I mean for Christ's sake Floss, that's supposed to be our money for when we get old.'

Flossie pulled a face. She knew that Douggie had taken a fall for Frank, but she didn't know the half of it. There was much Rita kept to herself. They both looked down the hall towards the front door when they heard a key in the lock.

'Hello, love. Why aren't you at school?' Ronnie came into the kitchen loosening his school tie.

'Mocks, Mum. Just did my second maths paper. We're allowed to come home if we don't have an exam in the afternoon.'

'Oh my God, of course. How did you get on?' Rita felt guilty. She'd been so worked up about Marilyn and this Frank Skinner business, she'd totally forgotten that Ronnie's exams were starting.

'Not bad.' Ronnie walked over to the kettle and flicked the switch on. 'All right, Flossie?' He slapped the old woman's backside as she stood up to rinse her cup and saucer. Though unlike his father in most ways, Ronnie had inherited the habit of touching women's backsides as a form of greeting. Flossie turned a powdery cheek so that Ronnie might kiss it.

'Hello, love. Behaving yourself?' she said.

Rita interrupted: 'What does "not bad" mean – good or just not bad?'

'No, Mum, I said it was all right. We got any of those chocolate rolls left?' Ronnie looked in the biscuit tin. 'I'm going up to my room. I've got revision to do. It's geography tomorrow.' Grabbing a handful of biscuits he walked towards the staircase. 'Bring us a cup of tea when the kettle's boiled, Floss.'

'Make your own bloody tea. Flossie's not here to run around after you,' said his mother.

'Two sugars,' he called as he made his way up the stairs with his football bag and biscuits.

'Little sod,' said Flossie indulgently.

'I'll do it, Floss, you get on with your ironing.' Rita poured boiling water on to the teabag in Ronnie's Crystal Palace football mug. She went upstairs and hovered outside his room. She always knocked now – he was a big boy – she couldn't just go barging into his room. She rarely accorded her daughter the same privilege even though she was five years older than her brother; Rita told herself that boys were different. He called for his mother to come in as he was putting a tape on the deck.

'I thought you were revising. You can't study with that music on.' Echo and the Bunnymen blared out of the speakers. 'Turn it down, Ronnie! . . . That's better, I can't hear myself think. Here's your tea, love.' She was so proud of him; he was doing eight O levels. Steve never took any exams, hadn't bothered to turn up for them, and Marilyn had been bloody useless, only got a couple of CSEs. Mind you, that was that rotten school she went to. Not like Ronnie, he'd done well at Juniors and got a place at John Kramer Boys' School up the road. Rita had been keen on the school because she'd always thought that the boys in their navy blue blazers had seemed so nice and polite when she saw them on the bus. Clever kids, quite posh too, some of them.

Rita closed his bedroom door behind her and walked across the landing to Marilyn's room. She hadn't come home last night. Not that that was unusual. Probably had some boyfriend she didn't want Douggie to find out about. Her dad could be funny about her boyfriends. She went in and sat on Marilyn's bed and picked up the toy rabbit she'd had since she was a baby. She remembered buying that rabbit with Douggie in the Bon Marché in Brixton for Marilyn's first birthday. It was bald now, and its ears had been sewn back on so many times, it had scars down the side of its head. Mr Babbit, she'd called him; she couldn't say her r's properly till she was about six. She was lovely when she was tiny.

Rita walked over to the wardrobe and studied the hanging clothes. She had to hand it to Marilyn, she bought lovely clobber. Rita stopped short when she saw a familiar sleeve poking out between the others. With a sharp intake of breath she said to herself, 'My bloody Frank Usher blouse, I've been looking for that.' She lifted it out and sniffed it. Smoke. Little cow. She couldn't find anything else that belonged to her in the wardrobe, but before she left the room, her eye fell on Marilyn's jewellery box on the dressing table. Opening it she saw the charm bracelet that Douggie had bought for Rita's twenty-first birthday and had been buying charms for every year since. It was gold and weighed a ton. She lifted out the bracelet and as she did so, something small and brown flew out of the box. She bent down and picked it up: it looked like a bit of dried shit. She sniffed it. 'If that's what I think it is . . .'

By the time Flossie left at about four o'clock, Rita had finished dusting and hoovering the downstairs of the house and was starting to get the tea ready. She was standing at the sink peeling potatoes and didn't hear Ronnie come into the kitchen. 'I'm starving,' he said, then stood close behind her and kissed her neck. Rita gasped in shock. 'Oh, it's you.

God, my nerves are terrible. Stick the kettle on.'

With one hand down the front of his trousers scratching, he walked over to the kettle, lifted it to check there was enough water and then flicked the switch. He was a tall, rangy boy with a slow walk: he moved like his mother. Sauntering over to the sink he hauled himself up on to the draining board next to Rita. His legs swung indolently against the cupboard.

'Stop kicking.' Rita slapped Ronnie's thigh with a wet hand. 'So, how did you get on with your revision?'

'Boring.' Ronnie was an amiable boy with a mocking smile, but so far in adolescence, rarely ventured beyond monosyllables.

'Never mind eh, they'll be over soon,' Rita consoled him absent-mindedly.

'Mum, I want to go to Spain at Easter with Spencer and his mum and dad.' Spencer O'Brien was Ronnie's best friend at school, a nice enough boy, but one who, in Rita's mind, bore the responsibility for Ronnie's bad language.

'Oh yeah, who's going to pay for that?' Rita eyed her son. 'You'll have to get a Saturday job, Ronnie, your father and I can't keep forking out.' Rita scooped up a handful of peelings and said, 'Mind your legs, I want to put this in the bin.' Ronnie raised his long limbs.

'Oh Mum, I already do a paper round. I'm pissed off with it. Anyway, you're not hard up.' His mother opened her mouth to speak, but realised he was teasing her.

'Our finances are none of your business. We shell out enough, that's all you need to know.'

'Yeah, but Mum I can't get a Saturday job, I want to go to university.'

'What's that got to do with anything? Anyway you've got to do your O levels first, then A levels.' Rita moved to the left of her double-sided draining board and started slicing the potatoes into slim sections and then into chips. Ronnie reached over a large, baboon-like hand and scooped up the strips, which he then piled into his mouth.

'Yeah, but,' he said through a mouthful of raw potato, 'I need to revise on Saturdays.'

'Since when have you revised on Saturdays? You're always playing football.' Rita slapped away the large hand that was descending on her potatoes again.

'Only in winter.'

Rita thought about this for a minute. 'Mmm. Well, you'd better speak to your father. Maybe when the football season finishes you can go and work Saturdays on the car lot. Sweep up, make the tea, get the sandwiches.'

'Put the bets on,' Ronnie added.

'Yeah, put the bets on.' Rita smiled at the image of all the lovely manly things that Douggie and Steve got up to at the car lot with Gully. Betting, looking at page 3, darts, lunch-times in the pub. It was a familiar order and one which comforted her.

'So what do you think about university, then? I think I'm doing all right in the mocks.'

'Doesn't mean to say you don't have to do anything till the actual exams.'

Ronnie grew impatient. 'Yeah, I know, but what do you reckon?'

'Well . . .' Rita paused. 'I think it's great, love. I don't think you should tell your father just yet though.'

'Why not?'

'He's not even keen on you doing A levels, Ronnie. Thinks they're a waste of time and that you should get a job. Learn a trade, an apprenticeship or something.'

'Why, so I can fix and flog cars like Dad and Steve? Or go out thieving. Yeah, he'd probably like that.' Imitating his father he said, 'Chip off the old block.'

Rita turned and pointed the small vegetable knife about an inch from her son's face. It dripped starchy water. Ronnie kept still.

'Don't you ever call your father a thief. I mean it.' She turned back to slicing the chips, her face flushed and angry. Just to push it, Ronnie said, 'Oh, so you're telling me he's honest?'

'Don't go getting all superior, Ronnie. Your father works bloody hard so you can have a nice life. The only reason you're sitting so pretty is because of your dad. Everything he's done, he's done for us. Look at this house—' Rita waved the knifed hand around her, indicating the large fitted kitchen with all mod cons.

'Oh come on, Mum, it's all bloody nicked.'

'I mean it, Ronnie. Just because you go to a good school, you think you're better than him. Well you're not. Do you think he would have done what he's had to if he'd been able to stay at school? He had to leave at fourteen, he's worked bloody hard, your father. Nobody gave him nothing.' She always reacted badly to this subject, not least because her true feelings mirrored her son's more than she cared to admit. But she always stood by Douggie. She had to. She couldn't let her kids run their own father down. It wasn't right.

Ronnie slid off the draining board and went to the fridge where he pulled out a pound of cheese and broke off a large chunk and put it in his mouth.

'Use a bloody knife, what's the matter with you? You're not an animal.'

'I'd rather be poor and not have to lie to my mates about what Dad does.' He put the cheese back in the fridge and pulled out a can of Coke and a hazelnut yoghurt.

'You don't have to lie. You tell the truth. Your dad's a car dealer. Nothing wrong with that.'

'And the rest.'

'Oh for Christ's sake just shut up. Get that bag off there, I want to lay the table for tea.'

'It's called dinner, Mum, or supper, not tea.'

'I swear to God, Ronnie, I'll crown you.'

Rita wiped her hands on her pinny and took the knives and forks out of the drawer. When Ronnie grumbled and went back up to his bedroom she smiled to herself. He was turning out so well.

CHAPTER THREE

Friends and Lovers

Tania Gull stepped outside her back door and bellowed down the garden to where her husband was working on the televisions he kept in his shed. He ignored her and unscrewed the back of a 22-inch Ferguson. Sometimes she went away. '*Gully*! For crying out loud, it's Douggie on the phone.'

'Why didn't you say so, silly prat?' Wiping his palms on his trousers Albert Gull put his screwdriver behind his ear and paused outside the shed to bend down and pinch the leaf of a plant which was springing up between cracks in the crazy paving. Spring was early. He sniffed his fingers and muttered, 'Lovely, lovely' as he made his way up the path of his long, narrow back yard. Squeezing past his glowering wife at the back door he said, 'Go down and give me plants a drink, Tania.'

'Water your own fucking plants.'

Albert Gull – 'Gully' to most people – had his own way of fighting the war on drugs. He'd loved a puff since his discovery of it in gaol in the 1960s, but he would have no truck with dealers and placed the ethical deterioration of the criminal fraternity squarely on their shoulders. Gully grew his own. For fifteen years, the back yard of his two-bedroom rented terraced home in Thornton Heath had been devoted to the cultivation of marijuana plants. They were now so well established that they seeded themselves abundantly, growing beyond the small boundaries of their allocated plot, springing up in cracks and even over the fence in next door's garden.

The old lady who lived there thought Gully wonderful for offering to weed her borders and insisted on calling him 'Albert dear' and making him tea.

Gully passed through the kitchen into the back room where one of Tania's sons from a previous marriage and his girlfriend lay slumped on the green Dralon sofa smoking dope. On the television a commentator was talking them through the speed-skating from Norway. The air was fetid; central heating on full blast and no windows open. On the floor at their feet were two cups of milky, sweet tea, green Rizlas and a pack of Benson and Hedges. Gully pulled a disgusted face. Being stoned was no excuse for being idle – Gully liked to use a buzz to get busy.

Closing the lounge door behind him, he settled on the bottom step and picked up the waiting receiver from the *faux*-teak hall table.

'Don't I even get Saturdays off any more?' he said.

'If that's going to be your attitude, don't bloody come to Sunday lunch, then.' In the thirty-five years of their friendship, Gully and Douggie had favoured keeping civil conversation, any conversation really, to a minimum. If you did have to communicate, it was more manly to shout the odds. Douggie was not only Gully's best and oldest friend, but the man who had kept him in work his entire adult life.

'A proper roast – beautiful. Tania doesn't cook anything that don't come out of a tin – do I have to bring her?'

'Rita did say to ask, but I don't suppose she'll be bothered either way. Steve's coming over with his bird, and the other two should be there if they're not off out with their mates – just family. I did want a word at some point, though, Gully – I need a favour.'

Tania came into the hallway, opened the cupboard under the stairs and pulled out the hoover which she plugged in next to Gully's feet.

'Hang on a minute, Doug . . .' Gully put his hand over the

receiver but could still be heard clearly. 'You don't fucking hoover from one week to the next, then the minute I'm on the phone you can't wait . . .' Tania muttered something about wanting to get it done before the football results came on because she had to check her pools coupon. 'Oh bollocks, you just wanted to ear'ole . . . can't stand the idea of not knowing what's going on, can you?' Gully's face grew puce and from behind his thick Coke-bottle lenses, the watery blue eyes bulged.

Tania shouted: 'And I bet you're arranging something behind my back now!' Her voice was choked with tears; she started on the Special Brew early at weekends. At the other end of the line Douggie smiled and carried on filling in a betting slip. Albert Gull enunciated loudly and clearly:

'*No, I'm poxy well not.* Douggie just rang up and asked me if I'd go to the auctions with him tomorrow because he's short on stock. That all right with you, noseache?' Tania threw down the vacuum cleaner and retreated sobbing into the back room.

'Oh fuck me, now she's crying again . . . listen Doug, I'd better go. See you tomorrow about twelve. We'll go down the battle . . .' A weasely note crept into his voice: 'Trouble is, the car got towed last night and I haven't had the cash to go down the pound . . .' It was always something with Gully.

'Call Zulu Cabs. Stick it on the account.'

'Cheers, Doug. I really appreciate it, mate.'

'Yeah all right. See you tomorrow.'

Douggie and Gully had developed their no-nonsense style of communicating at junior approved school in Basingstoke where they met in 1950. Unknown to them, they were neighbours in Stockwell and were sentenced and dispatched to the detention centre on the same day for the same crime: repeated thefts of lead. May the 1st would turn out to be an auspicious date in the life of Douggie Fisher. Ten years later to the day he would marry Rita Curtis.

But Gully was his first love. It was unspoken between them; they were tied for life. Douggie knew Gully was weak and that it was his role to protect him. In return Gully was faithful and true – had stuck by Douggie and worked for him during long periods when Douggie couldn't afford to pay him. Gully was a chancer, liked to sod about, wing it. Douggie, more solid, had grown tired of the stress of being totally bent. He had discipline and staying power, but Gully had mastered the art of enjoying life. Gully made Douggie laugh and in return he did his best to curb Gully's excesses. They needed each other.

Douggie had been able to go it more or less straight since he came out of Parkhurst in '75 and had felt it incumbent upon him to keep his best friend in legitimate work ever since. Gully had worked for him fixing up cars and running errands for the last ten years or so. Time punctuated only by Gully's occasional absences when he was foiled again in his attempts to pull off the perfect crime. 'You can't bloody help yourself, can you?' Douggie would laugh.

But Gully *had* developed a lot more self-control in middle age. He put his last spell in Wandsworth down to being pushed beyond unendurable limits. It had been the Saturday night after an afternoon lock-in at the Angel. He'd had about eight pints and was feeling like a king. He settled himself in with pie and mash (with liquor) and a cup of tea for the England/Scotland game on *Match of the Day*. Ten minutes into the match the picture started playing up. He fiddled with the aerial, but no joy. He gave the top and the sides of the set a few strategic bangs which would bring the picture back for a few seconds before it faded to fuzz again. He ran down to his shed in the rain, joint between his lips, and got inside and switched the light on. Drawing deeply he looked at the back sof eleven television sets which lined the walls. None of them were ready yet. The Ferguson, his favourite make, would take at least half an hour to put back together and he needed to get cracking.

Gully drove through heavy rain, confident and purposeful despite there being only one wiper on the van. He double-parked outside Radio Rentals where a drunk was sheltering in the doorway. Gully said, ' 'Scuse me squire' before pumping his crowbar in a series of thrusts at the plate glass. Bells ringing, glass flying Gully lifted out a 26-inch Pye colour set and put it in the back of the van. Not wanting to draw unnecessary attention to himself by revving off at high speed, he indicated, checked his mirror and pulled away slowly, leaving a gang of Saturday night revellers gawping in amused shock from the bus shelter across the road.

It was the timing that let him down. 'Always the bloody way,' he would later remark. The police were crawling around at closing time to stem the number of fights that inevitably spilled on to the pavements when the pubs turned out. Going robbing at quarter to eleven on a Saturday night in Thornton Heath High Road could be said to be raising the stakes. Gully had just turned left down Gonville Road and was thinking that he'd still catch the last few minutes of the first half when he saw the blue light flashing in his mirror. A squad car had been parked fifty yards from Radio Rentals outside McDonald's. Asked in Croydon magistrates' court if he regretted his actions, Gully replied:

'Yeah. No point nicking a telly and leaving the lead for the aerial behind.'

Rita always looked forward to Sunday mornings. Although she had the dinner to cook, at least she didn't have to go to work, or worse, do her twice-weekly run to the New Covent Garden flower market at dawn. She liked to lie in bed and listen to her family moving around. Douggie, always up early to cook the breakfast on a Sunday, would bring her a cup of tea and a digestive biscuit in bed and there she would allow the tea to gently wake her up as the smell of frying bacon rose from the kitchen and the sounds of warmth between her children came through the walls.

'Piss off Ronnie, I'm in the bath.' Marilyn had come home at 8.30 a.m. after a night out and gone straight to the bathroom.

'Get out of there, you slag. I need to get ready to go to football.'

'Oh use downstairs or go in Mum's room – I don't feel well,' Marilyn whined.

'Dad's taking a crap, he'll be ages and I don't want to wake Mum up.'

'Too late for that, the racket you two are making. And watch your language, it's disgusting,' Rita shouted from her bed.

Her son appeared, looking sorry and a bit desperate. 'Don't stand there crossing your legs Ronnie, go to the toilet.'

'I'm going to make a smell though, Mum.'

'Charming.' Smiling at her pyjama–clad son, Rita propped herself up on pillows and pulled the supplement from the *News of the World*. Turning to the Stars, she read Ronnie's horoscope to him through the bathroom door: '*Capricorn – Blue eyes mask a love that can be so right for you now. Jupiter hits your work chart and you blaze a trail to the top*' – oh that's good, that'll be your mocks – '*but watch jealous co-workers. Destiny shows a picture of a house in a foreign country.*' Yours are all right, what do mine say? '*Taurus . . .*' Rita muttered the words to herself then tossed the magazine aside tutting, 'Load of rubbish' before chuckling over a story on the front page about a vicar who had been involved in a threesome with two local girls. 'Good for him,' she said softly to herself.

Marilyn walked into her mother's bedroom in a short silk dressing gown with a towel around her head, clutching her stomach. 'Mum, I don't feel well.' Rita didn't look up and offered the standard maternal response.

'Why, what's the matter with you?'

'My stomach's killing me.'

'Got your usual?'

'No,' Marilyn replied irritably. She hated the way her mother always called it 'your usual'; why couldn't she say 'period' like everybody else?

'Don't be so bloody ratty. You probably just need to go to the toilet.'

'I've been.'

'Well then, I don't know, Marilyn, I'm not a doctor. I'll tell you something though, you could do with eating your dinners and getting some sleep – you're losing too much weight.'

'Oh, I can't win with you.' Marilyn's voice started to wobble. 'First I eat too much, then I'm not eating enough.'

Marilyn had always been a plump child, teased ruthlessly by her brothers and always being told by her slim-built mother to stop 'stuffing your face'.

'Yeah but Marilyn love, why can't you just be normal – you're either eating me out of house and home or going for days without food.' Rita looked at her daughter's dilated pupils and the red-rimmed glassy eyes filling with tears. Her skin looked sallow and grey.

'I'm tired that's all, I've just come in.'

'Well stop bloody moaning and go to bed, then.'

'I can't sleep.'

Rita rolled her eyes. Her daughter drove her up the wall. She was almost twenty-one, it was time she left home. Staying out all night, God knows with who, then walking her arse in with the milkman and crying her eyes out. Rita had had enough. Ronnie walked back into his mother's bedroom.

'Ugh, you stink, dirty bastard. Open a window.' Marilyn screwed up her nose, to which Ronnie drew a fist.

'Pack it in,' Rita said. 'It's Sunday morning. Get out of my bedroom the pair of you.'

'No one gives a fuck about me round here,' said Marilyn, stomping off to her bedroom and slamming the door.

Rita slipped on the red satin housecoat which matched her nightie – birthday present from Douggie last year, Marks, top of the range – and sat at her white three-mirrored dressing table with the detail of cherubs picked out in gold paint. She brushed her hair. It was so thick, she had to brush it for a good couple of minutes each morning just to stop it looking like a bird's nest. Douggie loved her hair, liked her to wear it long but, as she pointed out, 'I'm the one who has to wash it and blow-dry it, Douggie. And anyway, I'm not going any longer than shoulder length, I'm too old.'

Rita came into the kitchen as Douggie balanced two eggs on a fish slice and slipped them on to a plate already filled with bacon, sausage, tomatoes and fried bread. A low winter sun was shining through the windows, casting a glow over Douggie's bald pate.

'E'are love, sit down. What's the matter?'

'Oh, just those two fighting all the time. They don't give it a minute's rest. I'm fed up to the back teeth with it. Marilyn's always moaning. It's that stuff she smokes.'

'Nah, don't worry about 'em, they're all right.' Douggie sat down and immediately folded a rasher of bacon around some sausage and egg and collapsed it into his gaping mouth. Articulating and masticating at the same time, he went on: 'She's young, she's enjoying herself.'

'She's not enjoying herself, Douggie, she's upstairs crying her bloody eyes out. What does she get up to all night anyway?'

'Clubs these days stay open till six in the morning. Not like our day, babe.'

'Yeah well, you'd know all about that, being the expert.' Rita carefully cut up her breakfast and ate slowly. Douggie didn't reply. Phyllis Nelson was singing 'Move Closer' on

Capital Radio. 'Oh, turn it up, Doug. I love this one,' Rita said.

Ronnie came rushing into the kitchen. 'Mum, I can't find my football socks.'

'Airing cupboard.'

'Eat your breakfast, it's going cold!' his father shouted after him as he disappeared back up the stairs.

'I'm late for football, Dad, I can't. Spencer will be here in a minute.'

'Fucking Spencer can wait, I've just cooked that.' A small rivulet of runny yolk ran down Douggie's chin.

'Dad, I can't. Kick-off's at 10.30, I gotta go.' Ronnie ran back down the stairs three at a time and grabbed his Harrington windcheater from the banisters.

'Put your big coat on, Ronnie, you'll catch your death out there,' said Rita. Ronnie ignored her. A car horn tooted outside. 'See,' he said to his father.

'Well make sure you're in the pub before lunch, then. I don't want you coming back here and getting under your mother's feet when she's trying to get the dinner ready.'

Ronnie ran round the table and kissed his mother, who looked up absent-mindedly and said, 'Bye, love. Good luck.'

Douggie concentrated on his breakfast. Head down, elbows out, he purposefully sliced and mounted chunks of fry-up on to his fork. He used chewing time to spread butter on thick slices of white bread. Crumbs everywhere. In between mouthfuls, draughts of strong tea helped to wash it down. When the last of the tea had been swallowed, he put his knife and fork together leaving just two bacon rinds on the big empty plate, wiped clean with his last half-slice of bread and butter. Douggie smacked his lips and exhaled deeply, rubbing his belly with pleasure and relief. Rita smiled. He was a good eater, her Douggie.

He caught her looking at him. 'What?' he said, laughing.

'Nothing.' She laughed back. Her husband leaned across the table and looked into her eyes, seeing the challenge there.

She'd always been a stroppy cow, Rita – he loved it. He drank in his wife's face, the eyes puffy from sleep, and the hair still tousled. Douggie's sated belly made him feel suddenly vigorous. He flared his nostrils and, stretching his arms behind his head, inhaled deeply with anticipation. He reached under the kitchen table and moved both hands up Rita's red satin nightie and along her legs until his hands closed round her flanks and squeezed. No mucking about.

'What's Marilyn doing?' Douggie raised a suggestive eyebrow at his wife. Rita's smile spread slowly across her face.

'Gone back to bed, I think, or writing in her diary what a cow her mum is.'

'Dirty cow, more like. Come on.'

'Douggie we can't go back to bed, she'll hear us.' Rita made a pretend attempt to move the hands that were closing inwards across her thighs. He dug his fingers in tighter.

'Never mind about upstairs, come here.' He stood up and drew his wife towards him, pushed aside his plate and raised her up on to the end of the table. Lifting up the hem of her nightie, he positioned himself. Rita giggled, so Douggie leaned forward and closed his mouth over hers, whispering, 'Sshh, try and keep the noise down for a change.'

Rita stood in the kitchen carving the joint of beef. Frank Sinatra was singing, 'Don't you know little fool, you never can win. Why not use your mentality, wake up to reality . . . but each time that I do just the thought of you, makes me stop before I begin . . .' Putting the carved meat on her hostess trolley, Rita looked around her kitchen and sighed with happiness. She loved the new splash tiles Douggie had put up for her along the back of her counters. Midnight blue looked good with the wooden cupboards – really classy. Lifting the lids off two saucepans simultaneously she checked her sprouts and carrots. They'd be ready about the same time as the Yorkshires. Just right.

This was close to a perfect moment for her, alone in the house waiting for her family to come back from the pub for their Sunday dinner. She liked to put her records on loud while no one was around, have a bit of a singsong to herself. Maybe sit down for ten minutes for a quiet bottle of Guinness and a fag while she read the paper. It was bedlam when they came back from the pub. After dinner, the rest of the day would be spent clearing up and getting ready for work on Monday. Rita slipped off her pinny, lit a Rothmans, and looked at herself in the hall mirror. Twisting round she studied the rear view and decided her new velvet trousers from Marks made her bum look really good. She stuck it out and wiggled it about a bit. She still felt all tingly from the morning's exertions with Douggie on the kitchen table.

At the Duke's Head in Wallington, a small town about two miles closer to London, her family were gathered in a group next to the bar, shouting over the noise of the crowded pub. Slim, muscular and half a head taller than his father, their elder son Steve was trying to persuade Douggie that big luxury cars were a thing of the past and if they wanted the business to pick up they should start to get a few newish Japanese models in. 'No one wants to part with the dough for Jags these days – they're too heavy on the juice and insurance.' Steve hitched his trousers up and winked at the barmaid as he handed her his empty glass for a refill. The look on Douggie's face suggested that the sun was setting on the glory days of second-hand car dealership.

'Yeah, well, the game's changed since I started. It's time I moved on anyway. Made way for you. You'd manage all right with Gully, wouldn't you?' Douggie kept his eyes firmly on his pint as he asked.

'You're not serious about Frank's club, are you? You're bloody mad.' He laughed. 'Anyway the old lady won't have it. Another pint, Dad?'

'Your mother will bloody well do as I say at the end of the day, Steven.' It was a show of masculine strength that neither really believed, but Steve nodded in agreement anyway. He was fond of the old man.

Next to them in the group stood Steve's girlfriend Shelley, slim, immaculate and silent, and Ronnie, Marilyn and Gully. Ronnie was telling an impassive Shelley about the match he had just played, talking her through the second half when he headed the ball into the path of the striker who banged it home: 'Ah, it was excellent.' Gully coolly passed Marilyn a brown paper bag full of his home-grown, which she swiftly placed inside her coat pocket. 'Cheers, Gully.' She thanked him sheepishly, watchful of her father.

'What's the matter with you, got the 'ump?' Gully put his arm around her as she kicked a dog-end around on the floor.

'I need to move out. I can't stand it living at home any more and working with Mum is doing me 'ead in. She treats me like a fucking kid.'

'Well, why don't you move out then and stop fucking moaning. And swearing. Sounds terrible on a woman.'

Gully was fond of Marilyn – always had a soft spot for her. Quite advanced for her age too, old head on her shoulders. He could still remember catching her when she was about nine years old standing by the ice-cream van, letting the Italian inside it touch her little tit for a free 99. TONY SUPER-MAN OF STOCKWELL he had written in big letters on the side of his van and a blue and red plastic model of Superman in flight across the top. The kids loved it. Gully had always sus-pected he was a bit of a nonce and so he pulled him through the little window of his ice-cream van and nutted him. Well he had to, didn't he? Marilyn had dropped her ice cream and burst into tears, screaming, 'Don't tell Mum, Gully, don't tell Mum!' And of course he didn't – wouldn't be right to break a promise to a kid. He could remember walking her back to the flats, holding her little hand while she sobbed her heart out. When Rita opened the door of the flat Gully explained, 'Some coon nicked her lolly.'

Little by little the men in the group shifted round, swapping partners in conversation. Only the two women stood on either side of the group alone. 'Go and talk to your brother's girlfriend.' Douggie nudged Marilyn.

'Stuck-up cow, she doesn't talk to me, why should I?'

'Behave yourself, go and talk to her.'

She walked over to Shelley who stood ramrod straight staring ahead, her long, almost white blonde hair falling in a curtain down her back. Marilyn refused to accept everyone else's opinion that she was shy. She peeled the wrapper from a fresh pack of Embassy Number One and offered one to her. 'How's it going at the salon, then?' she said. Shelley was a beautician at Dickins & Jones.

'Yeah it's all right, thanks.' Shelley pulled her gold lighter from her bag and they both paused to light cigarettes.

'How long did you have to train to be a beautician?'

'Four months, but there's loads of different courses. Depends if you want to do electrolysis and vein removal or not. Then it gets more complicated. And expensive. But if you just want to do the basics – you know, facials, waxing – you can do a ten-week course.'

'I might do that. I'm fed up working in a flower shop. Especially Mum's. I couldn't pay for it though, I'm skint.' Shelley looked at Marilyn with a blankness that set Marilyn's blood pumping. Why did her brother always go out with such dopey tarts? They were all the same. Looked good, but sod-all to say for themselves.

'Croydon College must do courses though, don't you think?'

'I wouldn't know. My dad paid for me to go to a private college . . .' Shelley was off: the lovely training school in Dorking, René Guinot products, cathioderme facials, the benefits of Slendertone. Marilyn's mind began to go to work as she got a rush of the coke she'd taken the night before. She suddenly felt bright and buzzy – the opaque gloom that had dogged her all morning was giving way to a second wind, a soaring of the imagination that lifted her spirits. Yeah, a beautician. Why not? She could end up being a beautician for someone famous, you never knew, or maybe do make-ups for the telly. Excitedly she spun round and pulled on her father's sleeve: 'Dad, Dad, Dad, Dad, *Dad*!'

'Yeah, all right, mind me pint. What's up?' Douggie smiled to see his daughter cheering up.

'I want to go to college, Dad, and be a beautician, Shelley says you can do it in ten weeks and you wouldn't have to pay. I could go to Croydon College and get a job in a bar in the evenings or maybe move up to London and get a flat. I could move in with Michelle and if I did have to borrow some cash I could pay it back because you can get good money if you work in one of those top salons in the West End . . . maybe I can come and work at the club if you buy it.' Marilyn speeded on incoherently while her father listened indulgently, studying his daughter. Beautiful – just like her mother – especially now she'd lost her puppy fat.

'Yeah all right, slow down.' Douggie lifted his palms as if to shield himself.

Marilyn raised her glass, chinked it against her father's and winked. 'Here's to new beginnings for both of us, Dad.'

'Let's hope so, Dewdrop.' And he winked back.

Result, thought Marilyn. If he was calling her Dewdrop it was a good sign. Her childhood nickname usually made her cringe, but if she was after something . . . In a rush of adrenalin she could feel the layers of a tired way of life peeling away, the possibilities unfolding: getting out of the suburbs, away from these people. Especially her mother. When her father looked around at everyone's empty glasses and said, 'Right, are we all fit then? Time for dinner', she could hardly wait to get back and hand her notice in.

CHAPTER FOUR

Another Day, Another Dollar

Angel Motors, the seat of Douggie Fisher's empire, sits squat against the Brixton one-way system on Stockwell Road, its tall red metal doors, brick surround and wide forecourt lending the appearance of a fire station, which it had been before the London Fire Brigade consolidated its smaller stations into the main Lambeth site up on the Embankment. The wide but shallow forecourt allows only enough room for Douggie to display his 'hook' cars, the very flash or the very cheap to pull in passing trade. Beyond the pinned-back doors about twenty or so cars are parked neatly around the large showroom. It lacks the potted plants, carpet tiles and magazine-strewn coffee tables of new car dealerships, but its clean white walls, high ceilings and painted floor keep it a few notches above Douggie's rival used-car traders in the area, most of whom get by with just a few square feet of asphalt and a prefab hut. Hanging baskets festoon the pub next door and give the site a pastoral touch uncommon to South London – on a good day, with the sun shining and the multicoloured bunting flickering in the breeze, it can even look inviting.

Douggie had won the lease to the showroom in a poker game in Parkhurst two months before his release in 1975. George Allen, whom he'd won it off, took the loss quite well, saying it was no good to him as the lease only had three years to run and even with time off for good behaviour he would be detained for at least another seven. If Doug could evict the druggies that had been squatting in it for the last year and a half, he was welcome to it. Douggie, though chuffed by his win, had protested, saying he couldn't possibly take such an asset from a mate, but George had been firm. It was no bloody good to him, he insisted. Douggie would have to renegotiate the lease with the council when it ran out in '78, but it gave him a couple of years to get on his feet.

In the event Douggie's belief that 'everything turns out OK in the end' served him well. The resident squatters took very little persuasion when Douggie arrived mob-handed a week after his release with his two brothers Lawrence and Bert, and Bill, the landlord from the Angel next door.

Douggie's office was a glass booth to the left of the entrance. Though he had some 700 square feet in total and a basement of only slightly smaller dimensions beneath, his office was confined to a ten by twelve partition where he kept his receptionist Vivienne, his own desk and telephone, two extra chairs for customers, a dartboard and a display of KP peanuts from the pub next door. Douggie liked to peel off a packet a day and slowly reveal the breasts of a woman, usually looking wet on a beach somewhere, on the card beneath. He went mad if anybody touched his peanuts. He calculated that each hanging card holding twenty-eight packets lasted a month, allowing one for each weekday and two packets on a Saturday morning. He didn't work Sundays, so it kept the maths nice and simple.

A small portable television shared space with a spider plant on top of a four-door gunmetal filing cabinet. He only kept the telly for watching the racing. You'd be surprised, he used to say to Rita, how many people wonder how their horses are getting on when they're supposed to be concentrating on buying a car. On the few remaining inches of spare carpet stood a Calor gas heater which emitted such a noxious gas, Vivienne said she had to smoke to cover up the smell. He tried to impose a smoking ban once, but it had become impossible to enforce with Vivienne glaring at him and customers constantly lighting up.

Steve was officially employed as the sales manager – on the books, PAYE and everything. He would sit behind his father's desk, putting together stock lists for the weekly *South London Press* ad and making sure all the log books and MOT certificates were in the proper plastic folders. When he wasn't doctoring a car's service history in his small, neat handwriting, he liked to sit with his feet up on the desk reading the *Sporting Life*. Douggie thought it a waste of time to give Steve a phone and a desk of his own, especially as Douggie liked to move around a lot, talking to customers and keeping an eye on the chancers who would wander in off the streets. Gully used to like to crawl up from the basement for daylight and to drink coffee in the office, but Douggie got annoyed if there was grease on his furniture. 'Puts the punters off, a filthy sod like you hanging about. Get back downstairs.' The basement was Gully's domain. He had 500 square feet to himself and a great stereo system that Steve had put together from a lorryload of JVC equipment that had come their way. Gully listened to Elvis and Jim Reeves a lot. Steve said he would never have bothered rigging it up if he'd known Gully was going to play 'Distant Drums' all day.

The basement was accessed from the showroom by a curving car-park-style ramp where cars could be driven down for repair work and storage. Taking up a good quarter of the space were seventeen pinball machines that had sat there since 1982. When former site owner George Allen had come out of Parkhurst in the October of that year, he'd taken over an ailing amusement arcade in Herne Bay on the Kent coast in his attempt to make an honest living. Under his sterling leadership it went into liquidation five months later. He said he'd never open a seaside arcade in the middle of winter again. Desperate for cash, he asked Douggie if he wanted to take the pinball machines off his hands. If Douggie could get there with a lorry before the bailiffs turned up, he could have the lot for £3,000. Douggie, feeling it was high time he repaid the favour, agreed, chucked in an extra £500 for old times' sake and turned up in Herne Bay one Friday night.

Douggie, Steve, Gully and George had sat in the Lord Palmerston opposite the Victorian Herne Bay pier until after closing, drinking pints of mild and bitter and playing crib. George had bribed his two sons with £20 each to load the machines – 'Lazy gits, don't want to do anything to help their old man.' At 11.30 p.m., all six men in various states of inebriation had locked themselves in George's arcade, turned the music on and in a semi-darkness lit only by lights from the pinball machines, emptied the money out of them all into buckets. George counted the coins into 10p and 50p bags while the other five loaded the machines on to the lorry, having first to carry them the length of the pier. By adopting a totally casual air, it was unlikely they would arouse suspicion. Most people who were out at that time of night were too pissed to notice.

When all the pinball machines were safely on board, the assembled men sat down on the ghost train carts and drank a bottle of whisky from chipped mugs. George started filling up after his third, having a job to keep the tears back as he contemplated his failure. Douggie kept slapping him softly on the back as if he was winding a baby and repeating, 'It'll be all right mate' over and over while he choked back a lump in his own throat.

After their rescue from the clutches of the bailiffs, Douggie had never sold the machines on – most of them were easily traceable, and five years later they were in the exact spot where they'd been unloaded. Rita and Steve told Douggie it was foolish to keep that much hot gear in the basement, but to Douggie the pinball machines were a symbol of friendship. You never knew, he said, George might get back on his feet one day, get another arcade and when he did, Douggie wanted to be able to sell them back to him – he could have the lot for a grand. Officers from Brixton police station often popped in for a quick shufti round the showroom but they never ventured into the basement; they knew Douggie's form but villainy, like anything else, is a relative business.

All things considered, Douggie wasn't much trouble. There might be the odd consignment of stolen goods through the showroom, but he never, never had anything to do with drugs and besides, he helped keep at least a few of the local kids off the streets by giving them cash jobs – picking up parts, washing cars, running errands. Douggie Fisher considered himself something of a leader in the community and was pleased to offer what service he could. His favourite officer of the law, PC Rowland, or PC Plod as Douggie liked to call him, would often sit in Douggie's glass box and agree that what the kids lacked these days was a work ethic. 'If they can get the money by doing an honest day's work, they're not as likely to go thieving,' Douggie would say. PC Rowland tended to go along with Douggie on most issues, though they'd recently had a bit of a falling out over the abolition of the GLC. Douggie didn't agree that it was bad news for London.

'Good bloody riddance. Fucking rates I have to pay here just so they can give it away to every spade and shirt-lifter that tries to touch 'em for a grant. I wouldn't mind, but it's not as if any of the greedy gits with their hands out have done a day's work. Good luck to Maggie Thatcher, that's what I say.' Doug was all for the working man as long as he was white and actually went to work.

Douggie and Plod were about the same age and had an understanding based on years of professional acquaintance-ship. It had been a reluctant young PC Rowland that had been dispatched to Douggie's mum's on Brixton Hill to arrest him after the Mitcham warehouse job in 1971. Douggie had been touched by his civility and kindness and told Plod that he understood he was only doing his job, but the novice policeman had his misgivings about putting away a man with two kids and a third on the way. Douggie might have been dishonest, but he wasn't what you'd call dangerous.

All things considered, Angel Motors wasn't a bad place to work; mostly the atmosphere was good and Douggie was a generous boss. He could get a bit short-tempered if business was slow, or if he'd had a row with Rita or people weren't pulling their weight, but his outbursts were brief and he could usually be brought round by a good joke or a particularly nice page 3 girl in his paper. Quick turnover also cheered him up and would prompt him to take everybody next door to the pub for lunch. Anyone suggesting a pint and a cheese roll when the stock wasn't shifting, however, would quickly find themselves on the sharp end of his tongue. 'Buy your own fucking lunch, I'm not made of money.'

Douggie tore off February to reveal March's beauty on his Pirelli 1986 calendar. Where would he be at the end of the year? he wondered. He normally lived from month to month, but Steve was right, the business was changing. Nobody wanted the large luxury cars these days, least not second-hand. Douggie compromised by getting VW Golfs, Scirrocos and Renault 5s. The balance sheet was healthy but all the pride was going out of the job. Through the windows of his glass box he stared at the beautiful black Ford Consul which he'd picked up for next to nothing at the auctions and customised. It now had tinted windows, alloy wheels, new interior carpet and a fully reconditioned engine. It went like the bloody clappers too, but Douggie just couldn't sell it – made him wonder what the world was coming to. He was startled out of his thoughts by his son.

'Dad, geezer wants to know if we can drop down to seven on the Merc. Do you want to come and talk to him?'

'Cheeky sod. It's marked up at eight and a half.' Douggie chewed on his pencil. 'Mmm. Tell him he can have it for seven-nine then drop to seven-five if he gets stroppy.' Steve looked at his father, uncertain. 'What are you looking at me like that for? Go on, you're over twenty-one and white.'

'I'm not sure about this bloke, Dad. He's a bit heavy, says he's a mate of Frank's.'

Douggie leaned out of his chair and looked into the showroom. It took only a few seconds' flicking through his memory bank to put a name to the stocky figure. About five-nine and a good sixteen stone, the thick neck and rounded shoulders swathed in a brown leather jacket were unmistakable. 'Meat-head Mickey. Still a fat cunt.'

Vivienne tutted loudly and slammed shut her desk drawer. 'Sorry, Viv love, I forgot you were there. That typewriter's been so quiet this morning.'

Douggie got up and stood beside his son for a closer look at the back of the man who was leaning through the window of the Mercedes, studying the interior. 'You could never forget an arse that size could you?' Douggie nudged Steve reassuringly. 'Don't worry about him, he's no trouble. Frank always used him to put the frighteners on people. Couldn't harm a fly though, he's too fat to move. I'll come and say hello, but this is your one, you deal with it.'

Steve inhaled deeply and swept back his thick dark hair from his forehead, hitched up his trousers at the front and shot his cuffs so the links could be clearly seen peeking out the bottom of his jacket sleeves; like his father, he believed that a sharp suit was the first line of defence.

Father and son walked across the showroom side by side, hands in trouser pockets. They shared a certain swagger. The fat man didn't hear them approach as he'd already turned the keys in the ignition through the driver's window and was checking out the speakers on the car stereo. Seeing the generous backside before him, Douggie couldn't resist giving it a gentle tap with the end of his shoe. The fat man turned abruptly.

'What the . . . Doug! I didn't think you were here. How are you? Long time.' Douggie and Mickey pumped energetic handshakes.

'All right Mickey, still got plenty of puddin' on you, I see. What you doing round here then?'

Mickey shuffled and reddened slightly around the collar. Douggie knew exactly what he was doing there. Frank had sent him to check out business. Probably wanted to see how much money the site was pulling so he could get Douggie to top up his investment. Typical Frank, never came right out and asked a direct question when he could go through the back door. Worse still, he'd sent a lackey to do his digging.

'Frank said you could do me a nice motor,' Mickey blustered.

'Told you I was giving them away, did he?' Douggie smiled but an edge crept into his tone.

'Nah, nah, but you got to try and get a bit off, haven't you?' More bluster with a bit of nervous laughter thrown in.

'Well, you'll have to speak to my Steven. He's the businessman around here. Only keeps his old man on the firm out of pity.' Still smiling, Douggie fired Mickey an unequivocal look – don't mess.

Emboldened by his father's words, Steve took his hands out of his pockets, reached through the window of the car and removed the keys from the ignition. With the sound of the stereo suddenly cut, only a dull banging could be heard in the basement. Gully walloping the living daylights out of some engine, no doubt. Mickey shuffled, at a loss what to say next.

'Fancy a drive round the block, then?' Steve threw the keys up in the air between the men, giving them both a chance to catch, but caught them in a fist a split second before Mickey.

'Actually, I'm a bit pushed for time.' Mickey sized up father and son. Douggie stood quietly and let Steve talk.

'Shame to come all this way and walk away empty-handed for the sake of a five-minute spin.' He was beginning to enjoy himself. At a slim eleven stone Steve was no match for the massive middle-aged man, but he was quick, wiry and confident. A bold beginning could put your adversaries on the back foot very quickly.

Mickey looked at his watch and with bluff camaraderie said, 'Yeah, go on then son, why not?'

While Steve drove up Stockwell Road and then along Clapham Road to the Oval at breakneck speed, Douggie went back to his office and thought about Frank and the conversations he'd had with Rita; she might have a point. Douggie had to face it, he didn't have a poxy clue what Frank was up to really. Said he had some publishing deal, bringing in magazines from Europe. Said it was on the Stock Exchange and everything – couldn't remember the name, but Rita would know.

He picked up the phone and dialled the number of his wife's shop. Vivienne, seeing his intent expression, stood up, said she was going out to get a sandwich and did he want anything? Douggie absent-mindedly reached into his pocket for a fiver and said, 'Ham and piccalilli please, love.' As Vivienne buttoned up her raincoat to fend off the March winds and walked out of the box he called after her, 'Get us a copy of the *Financial Times* as well.' She turned and gave him a funny look, but then just shrugged and put her collar up.

Douggie tapped his pencil impatiently on the desk waiting for Rita to pick up the phone. 'Come on, come on.' Finally, Marilyn answered and in a quiet voice said, 'Hello, Rita's.'

'Put your mother on and try and sound a bit more cheerful when you answer the phone. No one wants to buy flowers from a misery-guts.'

Marilyn sighed loudly and banged the phone down on the table. He could hear his wife asking in a whisper who it was. Listening to her finish taking an order for a wreath, he tapped his pencil again. When she finally came on she was abrupt.

'What is it? I'm busy.'

'What's the name of Frank's company? You know, those magazines he was talking about.'

'Oh, how should I bloody well know. Ring him up and find out.'

'Yeah, you do know, I heard you talking to him about it and then in the car on the way home you said you thought it was a funny name. Come on Reet, think.'

'Oh Douggie, for crying out loud, you do pick your moments. Anyway, what do you want to know for?'

'I'm taking my wife's advice and doing a bit of research.' Douggie grinned at this little bit of charm and pulled off the day's peanut packet from the card; he was one pack away from a nipple. 'I'm going to check him out. I've just sent Viv out for a copy of the *Financial Times*.'

'Yeah, like you'll know what to look for once you get it.' Rita sat down on the little stool at the back of her shop, slipped off a shoe and, cradling the receiver between her chin and shoulder, rubbed her foot.

'Rita, you still there?' Douggie barked.

'Yeah all right, I'm thinking. Umm. Max something. Maxim I think, I can't really remember, Doug. Anyway what can you tell by looking in the paper?'

'Fuck all. But Ronnie'll know, he's doing O level economics, isn't he?'

'Think so, or politics, one of the two. I can't remember.'

'Well look, tell him not to shoot off until I get in. He hasn't got football tonight, has he?'

'Not tonight, no. Don't expect much for tea, I'm not in the mood for cooking a big dinner. It's been murder in here for a Monday, three funeral orders already this morning. Must have been a load of stiffs over the weekend.'

'Yeah, well, just tell that little sod not to go anywhere till I get in.'

'Yeah all right then, see you later.' Rita replaced the

receiver, slipped her shoe back on and stood up. She lit a cigarette but had to put it out almost immediately as another customer came in. She couldn't let Marilyn deal with anyone, the mood she was in.

Rita served the customer. It was the landlord from the Red Deer up the road, wanting a dozen roses for his wife. Rita said jokingly, 'What, you had a row, Pete?'

'Worse. I lost at cards last night. She's done her nut because I bet the money I was going to use for a new glasswasher behind the bar.'

'Yeah well, I'm not surprised.' Rita threw in half a dozen irises and a few nice leaves, wrapped them in some clear cellophane which she secured with a blue ribbon and said, 'Call it a tenner and give Pat my love.'

'Cheers Reet, you're a beaut.' He winked at her and closed the door behind him as he left, whistling. Rita watched him walk down the street and chuckled to herself, then looked at all the cuttings across the floor.

'Marilyn, I thought I told you to sweep this lot up. It looks a right bloody mess.' When no reply came she turned and called out to the back of the shop, 'Marilyn?' She walked out the back and slammed the door of the large refrigerator where she kept spare stock. She'd told Marilyn to keep it closed, it was such a waste of electric. From where Rita stood outside the toilet door she thought she could hear sniffing.

'Marilyn, what are you doing in there? Are you crying again?' Another loud sniff.

'No, I've got a cold. Go away, what are you doing listening outside the toilet? You're sick.' Hastily Marilyn unrolled the £10 note and put it back into her purse along with the small wrap. She wiped her finger along the back of the cistern to remove any trace of powder and rubbed the residue across her gums. She sniffed again, flushed the toilet and came out to find her mother staring at her quizzically.

'What?' Marilyn was all innocence. 'I told you, I've got a cold.'

'Well then you should have come in before breakfast if you weren't well. I'm getting fed up with this, Marilyn.' Rita lit two cigarettes and handed one to her daughter.

'I got in at half-one, actually.' Marilyn took the out-stretched cigarette. 'Cheers.'

'You little liar. You weren't in at four o'clock when I left for Covent Garden.'

Rita turned to study her face in the mirror over the big stainless steel sink, and wiped a streak of bright orange pollen from her cheek. 'You can't keep this up you know, you'll make yourself ill, out all night when you've got work in the morning.' Rita's tone was weary but not unkind. 'Honestly Marilyn, anyone else loped about the shop like you do and I'd have to sack them. You wouldn't get away with this, working in another shop, you know. You just think, "Oh, it's only Mum, it doesn't matter", but I shouldn't have to keep cleaning up myself, that's what I pay you for.'

'Well save yourself some money then.'

'What do you mean?' Rita turned quickly.

'I've had enough, Mum. I can't stand arguing the toss with you every day, I'm handing my notice in.' Finally she'd said it. She'd been trying to get her nerve up since yesterday lunchtime, but when she came home from the pub and found her mum so happy, she just couldn't do it. She knew Rita would be upset and it would ruin lunch, and by the time Gully finally left at 9 p.m. Marilyn was already on a train to Victoria.

'And do what exactly?'

'Go to college. I'm going to be a beautician.'

'Oh, *now* she thinks about college! Shame you couldn't have been so keen five years ago when you should have been doing your exams at school. And how are you going to support yourself? Don't think your father and I can afford to

49

keep you.' Plumes of smoke fled Rita's nostrils, her mouth too tightly closed for her to exhale.

'Dad says it's all right.' Marilyn raised a superior eyebrow. Done her.

'When did you speak to your father about it? He hasn't said a word to me.'

'Maybe he didn't think it was any of your business.'

Marilyn was charged now, challenging her mother. Rita drew deeply on her cigarette and pointed the fingers that held it at Marilyn's face. 'Don't you dare play me and your father off against each other.' Her eyes narrowed into slits. 'I know your bloody game.'

'Why don't you just ask him, Mum?' Marilyn felt strong and composed, her mind clear – it was good gear.

'Oh and he says he's going to pay for it, did he? You won't get a grant now, you're too old.'

'I don't need one, I can get a job.'

'Doing what? You can't even sweep the bloody floor for your own mother, don't think you'd last five minutes anywhere else. Besides, college doesn't start till September, it's only March. What do you plan on doing in the meantime, madam? If you think you're going to sit on your arse all day at home for six months you've got another think coming.'

'Well I'll fucking leave, then. And for your information, there's a ten-week course that starts in the summer term after Easter. I'm sick of it. I can't put a foot right with you, can I? Ronnie can do what he likes. I bet you'll support him if he goes to university, you think the sun shines out of his arse.'

'Yeah well your brother actually works hard at his schoolwork, not like you. I can count on one hand the number of times I saw you doing homework in your last year at school.'

'Oh what's the point?' Marilyn unbuttoned her overall and chucked it on the floor.

'Where are you going now?'

'Home!'

Rita thought of calling her back, maybe even apologising, but as Marilyn flounced out of the shop she turned to give her mother the finger. Rita chased her out on to the pavement and screamed after her down Selsdon Road, 'You can pack your bags while you're at it!' Marilyn kept walking at a brisk step, almost bouncing towards the bus stop.

Rita watched her young energetic body moving down the road and felt all the life drain out of her own middle-aged one. She turned and saw Mrs Singh from the newsagent's standing in her doorway. She'd come out to see what all the shouting was about. Rita rolled her brimming eyes heavenwards and shrugged apologetically as she walked back into the shop thinking to herself that Asians had the right idea, being strict. She bet Mrs Singh's kids didn't give her any shit.

'What do you mean she's gone?'

Douggie stood in the doorway of the kitchen, jacket half off and car keys in hand. His wife was sitting at the table wringing a limp and lifeless tissue, occasionally bringing it upwards to absorb a drop from her nose. Rita's eyes were glassy and the ashtray before her was full. The clock on the wall said 6.45 p.m., but unusually there were none of the noises and smells of dinner common to the Fisher household at this hour. Even though she'd already said she wasn't cooking much, he thought he'd at least get some egg and chips. Bollocks, he thought, hanging his jacket on the banister, I'm starving.

'Did she say where she was going?' he asked.

'No, it wasn't like that, we had a row about lunchtime. I got annoyed because she said she was chucking her job in and had spoken to you about going to college. Apparently you'd said it was all right without speaking to me first so I lost my rag and she stomped off home. I told her to pack her bags, but I didn't think she'd really do it, it was just temper talk.' Rita's facial muscles contorted with the effort of stopping another crying jag. 'Why didn't you say anything to me about her going to college?'

'Rita love, she only mentioned it in the pub yesterday. I just forgot, that's all. Probably just another of her five-minute wonders. Besides, you and Marilyn tell each other to sod off every other day. I expect she'll walk her arse back in the door tonight. She'll be round one of her mates love, don't worry.'

'All her clothes have gone.'

'What all of 'em? She get Pickford's round to pick them up?'

Rita didn't share the joke. 'She's taken all of her make-up and tom, all her bits out of the bathroom. She's gone, Doug.'

Douggie stood up and walked round the kitchen table and drew his wife's hot face and tangled hair to his chest where she had a little sob. He lowered his face on to her brow and kissed it, his fingers stroking the thick, coarse hair. When her breathing quietened down he slowly prised her away and said, 'Listen, get yourself in the bath and I'll bring you a drink up. Just try and calm down. I'll ring round her mates. Anyway, she won't have gone far, she likes her comfort too much, that one.'

Rita sniffed, nodded and smiled wanly at Douggie. He was so lovely sometimes it could set her off all over again. She trudged slowly upstairs while he put together a little tray. He gathered together her cigarettes and lighter, emptied the ash-tray and gave it a rinse. He then took an already opened bottle of wine from the fridge, sniffed it and poured a large glass. He ripped off a square of kitchen roll and completed his tray with a packet of salt and vinegar crisps from the cupboard. As he started up the stairs the front door opened and his younger son came in.

'Where have you been, it's almost seven o'clock?' Douggie demanded sharply.

'Round Spencer's. What's your problem?' he responded righteously.

'Your mother's upset.' Douggie cut a slightly comical figure with the dainty little tray and Ronnie had to point and smile at him. 'It's not funny, your sister has packed her bags and left.'

'Great, can I have her room?'

'Get in that kitchen and don't fucking move till I come back. You're going to help me find her.'

'Oh, Dad, it's the World Cup qualifying rounds tonight.'

Douggie faltered slightly at this information and for the first time felt annoyed with his daughter. Fancy walking out on a big football night, awkward little cow. 'Well, we'll still have to make some phone calls. Find something in the freezer for dinner.'

'Hasn't Mum cooked anything?' Ronnie was shocked; there was always a plate of grub for him somewhere. Douggie shook his head, confirming the worst. It was a bad night – crucial match, missing daughter and no tea.

Douggie balanced the tray in one hand and knocked gently on the en-suite bathroom door. Rita called softly for him to come in and said, 'Aahh, Doug' when she saw his little tray.

Even though her face was wet from washing he could tell she was still crying. He'd never known a woman like it for tears. It wasn't that Rita was weak but she was just so emotional. He sat on the toilet with his tray on his lap and looked at his wife's naked body beneath the bubbles; he felt a wave of love so strong, his stomach turned.

'Was that Ronnie I heard?' Rita tried to steady her voice, get back to normal. Douggie handed her the glass and lit a cigarette for her, almost choking. He never could smoke, tried for years.

'Yeah, little sod. What's he doing coming back late on a school night?'

'Leave him, Doug. We don't want two walking out on the same day.'

Douggie loosened his tie and looked at her, but she wasn't in the mood for talking. 'You all right then? I'll let you get on with it and go and start ringing round.'

'Yeah. Thanks love, I'll be down in a minute.' Rita drew deeply on her cigarette and a piece of ash fell into the bath, dissolving the bubbles around it.

'Take your time. Do you want some dinner?' Rita shook her head. Douggie nodded at the tray. 'There's a packet of crisps on there if you want them.'

Back in the kitchen, Douggie found Ronnie eating a lump of cheese, his head in the deep-freeze, sorting through pies and bags of oven chips. 'What are you supposed to do with these things, do you have to defrost them first?' He held up two cod and parsley sauce in the bag portions. Douggie shrugged.

'Shall we just have some cheese on toast, Dad? The game'll be on in a minute.'

'Yeah, all right mate. D'you want a beer?'

'Yeah, nice one. What's happened then?'

'Marilyn and your mother had a row at lunchtime, Marilyn chucked in her job and came home and packed her bags. I expect she'll turn up when she runs out of money.' Douggie pulled two cans of Harp out of the fridge.

'Shame. About time she left home.' Ronnie sawed off four thick wedges of white bread from the fresh bloomer.

'You just keep your opinions to yourself. Anyway, she's probably round at Tricia's or Michelle's. Where are their numbers?'

'How would I know?'

'Well go upstairs and see if you can find her address book in her room. Get the one off the hall table as well.' The phone rang and they raised their eyebrows at each other. 'Go on, go and answer it and if it's your sister don't dig her out.'

Ronnie picked up the phone and Douggie could hear him say, 'Yeah, who is it?' He came back into the kitchen and said, 'Some bloke called Nelson Watts.'

'Nelson who?' Douggie went and picked the phone up. An educated voice at the other end said: 'Mr Fisher?'

'Speaking.'

'You don't know me, but I'm a friend of Marilyn's. I just wanted to let you know she was OK and not to worry. I understand she had a bit of an argument with her mother.'

Douggie was taken aback.

'Well, that's very decent of you, son. If you don't mind me asking, who are you?'

'Like I said, just a friend. Marilyn doesn't want anybody to know where she is, but I know how parents worry, especially about their daughters, and I just wanted to let you know she was fine. I'll try and get her to call you or her mother tomorrow. She's a bit upset at the moment, in the bath actually, she doesn't know that I'm calling.'

Douggie fidgeted uneasily: what was she doing in some bloke's bathroom with no clothes on?

'Where do you live, Nelson?'

'West Croydon.'

'Oh, just up the road then, that's good. Umm, the thing is, son, she's never mentioned you before.'

'Well, we haven't known each other very long. I was a bit surprised to come home from college and find her waiting on the doorstep.'

'Well look, give us your number so her mother can give her a ring. She's in the bath herself at the moment.'

'If you don't mind, Mr Fisher, I'd rather not. I think Marilyn would be upset if she knew I was calling you. I'd appreciate it if you didn't let on when she does get in touch.'

'Umm, yeah all right. So, do you go to work then?'

'Part-time. I study electrical engineering at Croydon College.'

'Oh, that's good, at least you'll have a trade.' It seemed odd circumstances to be having a chat about an unknown man's prospects but Douggie wanted to know who this boy was. Sounded nice, but what kind of name was Nelson?

'Look Mr Fisher, I'd better go, I think Marilyn's getting out of the bath. I'll make sure she calls.'

'Yeah, appreciate it, cheers.' Douggie put down the receiver and scratch his bald pate. Rita came down the stairs in her dressing gown, a towel round her head. 'Was that her?'

'Yes and no. Some geezer called Nelson, if you please. Says that Marilyn's with him and not to worry, he'll get her to call in the morning. Have you heard of him?'

'Nelson?' Rita walked into the kitchen followed by Douggie and poured herself another glass of wine.

'You haven't heard your sister talk about anyone called Nelson?' Douggie asked Ronnie, who was adjusting the aerial in the portable telly in the kitchen, trying to get the picture right before the game started.

'Nah, sounds like the sort of wanker she'd go out with, though.'

'Give it a rest, your mother's upset!' Douggie roared.

'What did he say, did he leave a number?' Rita took the towel from her head and shook her hair.

'No, sounded all right though, very polite.' Douggie grimaced and shook his head. 'Weird.'

'Well did he say where she was?'

'West Croydon. In his bloody bath, if you please.'

'As long as she's all right, I don't care.' Rita drew her first easy breath since coming home and finding her daughter gone.

'Can I have her room if she doesn't come back?' Ronnie put his hand down the front of his school trousers and scratched.

'No you can't and leave yourself alone. Go upstairs and get my fags for me please, they're in the bathroom. Take this towel up with you and hang it on the rail while you're at it.'

'Oh Mum, the game's starting!'

'Do as your mother tells you!' Douggie slammed his can down on the table as his son stomped up the stairs swearing under his breath. 'I'll kill her. Fancy him telling me she's in the bath. It's the last thing you'd say to a girl's father.'

'I've got to turn this bloody telly off, I can't think.' Rita poked the off button sharply, poured her glass of wine down the sink and, deciding on tea, flicked the switch on the kettle. Douggie swallowed the urge to bollock Rita about the importance of the World Cup qualifying round.

All was quiet in the kitchen for a few minutes, only the hum of the deep-freeze and the sound of Ronnie's feet above them. He came back into the kitchen with his mother's cigarettes, which he threw across the room. She caught them in a quickly raised fist. Good reflexes ran in the family. 'Oh Mum, what have you turned the telly off for?'

'I can't think with that racket. Go in the front room and watch it and don't get crumbs all over my suite.'

'You coming, Dad?'

'Yeah, go on then.' Douggie looked at his wife. 'Come on love, no point thinking about things too much. Sit down and watch the game, it'll take your mind off it. I'll stick the fire on.'

The Fishers' front room was long, and no expense had been spared on the décor. Douggie had knocked out one of the walls and put in french windows which opened on to the garden. A large, deep red Persian rug and a smoked-glass coffee table dominated the centre of the room. The gold-embossed wallpaper cost £12 a roll. Rita pulled the floor-to-ceiling deep greeny-blue, ocean-coloured flock curtains, fully lined, while Douggie lit the gas coal-effect fire and Ronnie switched on the 28-inch colour TV set. Rita placed cork coasters on the occasional tables next to the settee and Douggie's chair so their cans wouldn't make those nasty white rings on the wood. Real teak – G-Plan – you had to look after it.

After fetching herself a cup of tea and another can for Douggie, Rita settled back into the corner of the deep settee and poked Ronnie's sprawled legs with her foot. 'Done your homework?' Ronnie shook his head, only half listening to his mother and shouted out, 'Offside! That ref's a div.' Rita smiled and picked up the *TV Times* to see if there was anything on the other side; she could always take the portable into the bedroom.

She felt cosy in the front room with her husband and son, but she'd feel better still to have Marilyn upstairs in her bedroom with the music blaring, or more usually on the phone to one of her mates in the hall, lounging on the floor with her feet up against the wall. Funny kid, always preferred the floor, never sat on a chair if she could help it. When she was little, she used to pull all her covers off the bed and when Rita came in with her milky tea of a morning she would find her curled up between the bed and the radiator, buried beneath a tangle of blankets and sheets.

The phone rang just as a free kick outside the penalty area was about to be taken. Ronnie and Douggie, glued to the set, ignored the ringing and Rita had to get up to answer it. She walked slowly, having lost her sense of urgency now that Marilyn had been in touch.

'5419. Hello?' The line cracked and popped with the interference of a long-distance connection. There was an echo to the caller's voice.

'That you, Rita? It's Frank, can I have a word with Douggie, please?'

'He's not in at the minute. Where are you?' Rita spoke slowly and loudly, as if Frank were deaf, while studying her face in the hall mirror. Her eyes were still puffy.

'I'm in Amsterdam on a bit of business. I get back in tomorrow and wanted to meet up with him. He said he'd be in, he's expecting me to ring.' Frank sounded shirty.

'Like I said he's not here and I don't know when to expect

him. Sorry.' Her tone didn't sound in the least bit sorry; she wasn't going to be pushed around. She picked up the *Financial Times* Douggie had left on the hall table and folded it into one of the roomy pockets of her dressing gown.

'You must have some idea when he's coming home.' Frank's voice became aggressive.

'I'm his wife, Frank, not his keeper. You'll have to ring in the morning, I'll tell him you're trying to get hold of him. Bye.' She put the receiver down before he could reply and said to nobody, 'Bloody cheek.' She waited by the phone for a few seconds and just as she thought, it rang almost immediately. She picked it up and put it down again quickly. It felt good to know that Frank would be fuming at the other end.

When she walked back into the front room father and son were engaged in half-time analysis. 'Hoddle's playing like a bloody fairy. Who was that on the phone?'

'Frank calling from Amsterdam. It was a really bad line. He's going to call back in the morning.'

'What did he want?' Douggie sounded anxious.

'How should I know? He said he'd call back.' She threw the newspaper at him.

Douggie hesitated and decided not to push it. There had been enough upsets for one day. He turned to his son: 'Right then, professor, I want to use your brain.'

CHAPTER FIVE

High Days and Holidays

The Skinners had invited Douggie's family for Easter; leave straight after work on Thursday, they said, make a long weekend of it. Rita had, however, insisted that Good Friday, like Christmas, was inviolable and that it would be spent at home. Frank Skinner could 'wait till we get there'. It was tradition in the Fisher household for one of the kids to get on their bike and cycle down to the baker's in Foxley Lane and buy the warm, scented, oven-fresh hot cross buns for breakfast. Since Ronnie had a paper round, the task usually fell to him. Meanwhile, one of the other two would put together the big tray with a pot of tea, five cups, tea plates and knives to take up to their parents' bedroom. Rita and Doug would prop themselves up on pillows while their three children fidgeted about like old dogs looking for a comfy spot on the bed, waiting for the chocolate to be dished out. Though Steven had left home four years previously, at twenty-five he still came home for Good Friday morning to get his egg from his mum. Shelley had sulked, complaining that he should spend the holidays with her now that they were living together, but he'd said, 'Don't keep on, Shelley, it's family. I have to be there.'

Rita handed out the eggs while Douggie read his copy of the *Sun* and noisily masticated a toasted bun dripping with butter, slurping his tea noisily between bites. Marilyn was given a Caramac egg and Ronnie a Smarties one. Marilyn complained that Ronnie's was bigger than hers, but her mother pointed out that Caramac eggs only came in one size and as she didn't eat any other chocolate she'd just have to lump it. Doug wasn't keen on chocolate so Rita usually bought him a Dick Francis novel or a shirt from Marks. Rita always got the biggest egg, usually a Black Magic or Dairy Box from Douggie and the children – not that she ever got to eat much of it. Every year Ronnie managed to polish most of it off and would be told by his mother he was 'a dreadful guts-ache'.

Marilyn lit a cigarette and flicked the ash in her saucer. 'Do you have to do that in here?' her father asked, but Rita shushed him and lit one herself in a gesture of support. One of the conditions for Marilyn coming home had been her liberty to smoke and Rita had thought this a small request, especially as in all likelihood she'd picked up the habit from her mother in the first place. 'I don't want you smoking any of that other stuff though, Marilyn, do you understand?' Rita had warned her.

So now Marilyn was slumped at the foot of her mother's side of the bed looking a bit green around the gills. She'd had a particularly good session in Rumours wine bar in Croydon the previous evening with four of the girls she would be attending college with. They'd met at the registration session and immediately retired to the nearest bar afterwards. When Douggie lifted a cheek and farted resonantly beneath the covers, Marilyn made a retching motion and Rita reacted with undue force, slapping him. Through gritted teeth she hissed, 'Jesus Christ.' Shaken from his sleepy state, Douggie came as close to thumping her as he had in the twelve years since he raised his hand to her for the first and last time. On that memorable occasion, she had responded by whacking him across the temple with the steam iron she was holding. Seven stitches later in the casualty department of St George's Hospital, Douggie vowed never to strike his wife again.

'What is the matter with you?' Douggie asked his wife.

'Nothing.' She reached over to her nightstand and switched on the clock-radio.

Marilyn and Ronnie looked at each other and pulled faces. Of the assembled four, only Doug was looking forward to the weekend at Frank's. Marilyn had insisted that she wanted to be with her friend Nelson, but Doug had been firm and said she wasn't going to spend the holidays with some man they'd never met before and knew bugger all about. Ronnie had been bolshie ever since Rita put her foot down and vetoed his trip to Spain with Spencer – he could wait until the summer when his O levels were over. For the time being, he should get his head down and do some work. Besides, if he wasn't prepared to get a Saturday job, she was buggered if she was going to pay for his holidays – they weren't made of money.

The group settled into a gloomy silence until they heard Steven's key turn in the lock downstairs. He came into the bedroom with a rolled-up newspaper, waving away the smoke. He looked at his sister but asked his mother, 'What are you letting her smoke in here for?'

'Oh, don't you start, come and give us a kiss.' Rita smiled up at her elder son as he bent down to kiss her. Shoving his little brother over so he could fit on the bed, Steven said, 'All right Dad, what's up?'

'Your mother's got the 'ump so we all have to suffer. Not even allowed to fart in my own bed now.'

'Don't take any notice of him, love. Here's your egg. How's Shelley?' Rita fished under the bed and pulled up his gift.

'She's having a lie-in. Oh Buttons, what a surprise, Mum!'

'You used to love Buttons.'

'I do, Mum, I do.' Steven looked at his puny little egg with its fragile cardboard surround and wondered. Had he really left a blonde in a warm bed at the crack of dawn for this? 'Any hot cross buns left?' Steven leaned back on his elbows and moved his head from side to side, clicking the bones in his neck. Marilyn dry-heaved again.

'There's some more downstairs.' Rita felt the pot. 'Tea's still hot, pour yourself a cup. I'm going to get dressed and have a tidy up. Come down and give me a hand please Marilyn when you're dressed.'

'Why do I have to do it? Why don't you ever ask him?' Marilyn pointed at her younger brother, now reading the sports pages and starting on his mother's egg.

'He's got exams in a couple of weeks.'

'So have I.'

'Yeah, but you're almost twenty-one and don't give me any housekeeping now you've packed in work, so you can help me out and do a few chores instead.'

The weariness in Rita's voice made her daughter bite her tongue. She settled for grumbling loudly and stomping off to the bathroom to get washed. Rita went into her own bathroom and after splashing herself with warm water, stared at the tired, middle-aged face in the mirror opposite. Her grey was showing through, she could do with a tint.

In the bedroom, Douggie enthused about the weekend. 'So, you and Shelley coming on Sunday for lunch, then? Supposed to be a fantastic drum old Frank's got, listed or something. Big bastard.'

'We haven't got anything planned for Saturday night, so we'll probably start out early. Should be a nice drive if this weather keeps up. I thought we'd drop down to Sunbury, pick up the M3, over to Bracknell then shoot straight up the M329 through Reading and over to Sonning.' Route planning was a favourite with the Fishers. Steven paused, 'What's the matter with the old girl, then?' He nodded towards the bathroom. Douggie shook his head and scratched.

'Oh, I don't know, she's always copping the arse'ole these days. First it was the club, then Marilyn, now the club again. There's no pleasing your mother sometimes.'

'Yeah, but women, Dad, they're not happy unless they've got something to moan about, are they? I mean, take Shelley.

It was beautiful in the beginning, all black stockings and knee tremblers, but once you're shacked up they go back to tights and asking you where you've been all night.'

Douggie laughed. It was good to know that the young suffered too. Ronnie looked up from the sports section to add his tuppence-ha'penny worth: 'What can you expect if you treat women like sex objects?'

'What would you know, you little poof?' Steven poked his brother in the groin and when Ronnie crouched over to protect himself started tickling and slapping him. Over cries of 'Get off you wanker!' Douggie teased, 'Proper little feminist, your brother. Thinks page 3 is *demeaning*.' Steven laughed cruelly.

'No I'm not. I just want a girl with a bit of personality and brains, not some tart who just thinks about clothes and make-up all the time.'

'You saying Shelley's a tart?' Steve pulled his bottom lip tight over his teeth and flared his nostrils. When Ronnie smirked, Steve raised a fist.

'Pack it in!' Douggie bellowed and slapped them both around the head with his paper. Now Ronnie was getting bigger, his fights with Steve had become nastier. He'd managed to hurt his elder brother a couple of times and Steven hadn't liked it, got a bit handy and slapped Ronnie back too hard. Douggie could still give both of them a good hiding if he needed to, but they were big now, getting strong. Douggie had butterflies every time it kicked off, wondering if maybe this was the time he wouldn't be able to control them. He pulled his pools coupon out of his bedside drawer. When they'd got too big to be pacified by sweets, letting them do his coupon had proven a good bribe: 'Fill that in, I'm going to have a shave.'

He found his wife with her head leaning against the glass of the bathroom cabinet. She looked up to give him a watery smile. He could see what was coming: 'You don't want to go, do you?'

'It's not just this weekend, Doug. It's everything.' Rita unscrewed a jar and began to rub cream into her neck. 'For the first time in years I feel all jittery again. I thought we'd finished with all this, we're settled now, it's supposed to get easier.'

'Well it's not going to get harder for you, is it? I'm not asking you to come and work at the club – you don't have to do anything.' Douggie held out his hands in supplication.

'But I've got this knot in my stomach like something's going to go wrong.' She carefully screwed back the lid on the jar and placed it back in the cabinet, sliding the door shut to reveal her tired face again. The quiet from the bedroom told them their sons had stopped talking football and were eavesdropping. Rita nodded at Doug to close the door. He pulled it quietly to and sat down on the toilet seat where he eased his wife on to his lap and gently rocked her. Rita's breathing grew deep. He pulled a length of paper from the toilet roll and offered it to her. 'Talk to me, Reet.'

'I'm all right. Maybe I'm just going through the change.'

'How can you be, you still have your periods don't you?'

'It's not as simple as that, Doug. Oh I don't know, I'm just feeling old. I'm not up to starting all over again, I don't want new things, I want what we've got. Now that Marilyn's back I don't want anything else rocking the boat.'

'Yeah, but it's not going to stay like this, is it? I'll lay you odds she'll have moved in with one of her mates by the time she's finished that course this summer. Steven's plotted up in Norwood and Ronnie's sixteen this year; they've got their own lives.' He rubbed some life into his wife's cool arms. 'We're going to be on our own soon, Rita, and I don't want us to wake up and find out we've got nothing to do when they're gone. We'll end up killing each other.'

'But a *nightclub*, Doug. I'm forty-six.'

'Yeah, you're forty-six and you're beautiful.' Douggie

shifted and eased her off his lap. 'You're a bit heavy though, love.'

'Charming.' Rita stood up straight, stretched, and brushed her hair in the mirror. She felt a bit better, but her stomach was still tight. 'Do you want to do me a favour?'

'Not really.'

'Nip down to the chemist in Wallington and get me a Harmony for my hair, please. Warm Chestnut Brown.'

'They're not open Good Friday.'

'The Indians in Manor Road are.'

'Yeah all right, when I've had a shave. What time do you want to push off, then?'

'Well, I want to have a bit of a clear up, and I've got a chicken for lunch, so about two, half-two.' Rita squeezed toothpaste on to her brush, then opened the door and called to her sons: 'Right, you two, downstairs. I want to get changed.'

Douggie sat in the driveway before they pulled away, going through the possibilities. It was a favourite pastime of his that he shared with his elder son – short cuts, back roads, routes nobody would dream of: 'We could drop down to Reigate and pick up the M25, but you don't want to sit on the motorway all afternoon, it'll be chocka with everyone going away – then we could always do Epsom, A3, pick up the M3 and shoot straight across . . .'

'This is already a nightmare,' Ronnie said to his sister.

'Don't start moaning before we've even got going,' his mother reproached him.

'Well, why couldn't I go to Spain with Spencer and his mum and dad? It's not fair.'

'You've got exams in a couple of weeks, you're supposed to be revising,' Douggie chipped in.

'Bollocks to that. I don't have to go to Spain not to do revision.'

'Shut up – you're giving my arse 'eadache.' Rita fished for her cigarettes in her bag and when Douggie looked at her she added, 'If you think I'm going all the way to Berkshire without a fag you've got another think coming.' Douggie did his best impersonation of a patient man but when Marilyn piped up, 'Oh good, does that mean I can smoke?', Douggie burst out, 'No it bloody well doesn't!'

'Well *she* is.'

'Just shut up, Marilyn.' Her father started the car.

'I don't know why you want us to come.' She was referring to herself and her brother, unusually united on the issue. 'All you do is have a go at us. I don't see the point.'

Rita raised her eyebrows at Douggie in that 'told you so' manner, and reversing out of the drive with undue haste he almost caught a boy on a bike coming around the bend.

'For crying out loud, Douggie!' He stopped the car and put the handbrake on.

'When everyone has finished digging me out, do you think we can just get a move on?' His wife and children fell silent, so Douggie turned on the radio and they became independently lost in their thoughts for a while. Ronnie pulled out his Walkman and sealed himself off from the other passengers. Marilyn leaned over the front seat and reached for her mother's cigarette: 'Give us a lug, Mum.'

It was a beautiful day; clear with a warm sun and a fresh breeze. Rita looked at the blackthorn in blossom along the motorway and thought of summer. She really should get cracking on the garden soon if it wasn't to overwhelm her by June. She hadn't bothered cutting back the roses the previous autumn and had a good few days' work just pruning and tidying the more straggly plants. She still hadn't started off her seeds in the greenhouse for planting out in May and could feel herself falling behind. Another reason for staying at home this weekend. The garden was too big for her to cope with on her own, but she had wanted the house so badly when she saw it, she didn't mind that there was a ninety-foot lawn to mow, a mature orchard and several raised beds and borders to tend. She'd added more to it in the five years they'd been in Purley, planting Dublin Bay climbing roses either side of the french windows and several clematis that were beginning to trail across the roof. In a couple of years when it all joined up it would be lovely.

She was curious to see Doreen and Frank's garden, had even gone to the library in Wallington on her half-day to find out about Gertrude Jekyll who had designed the grounds at Deanery Gardens. She found some black and white photos of the gardens taken in the 1950s and they looked fantastic. The house itself was an even bigger knockout: really old and full of character, designed by some bloke called Lutyens. She'd asked the librarian how you pronounced the name. If she was honest with herself, she'd probably have to admit that her nerves about the weekend were more to do with the effect that seeing such a pile would have on Douggie. He was terribly competitive and had only been able to rest in recent years because they had been doing so much better than all their friends. Some of them still lived in the council flats in Stockwell where they'd all started out and the ones that had got off the estate had managed only small semis or terraced houses. The Fishers were alone among their peers in having a detached home with four bedrooms, a big garden and a large attic space which had been turned into a den with a pool table for the kids to entertain their mates in. Seeing Frank's house would get Douggie all worked up again, set him off on some new ambitious scheme. There would be no backing out of this club business now.

Rita pulled down the visor and fussed with her hair in the vanity mirror. 'Do you think this colour has gone a bit red, Marilyn?'

'No, it's fine, it's just the light picking up the natural red in your hair. You could do with a hydrating mask though, Mum, your face looks a bit dry. You should come into the college and get a facial. We practise on customers on Thursday afternoons, I could do you for a fiver. René Guinot products and everything.'

'I can't leave the shop on a Thursday, Marilyn, not while I've only got your auntie Mave to help me out. Anyway, can't you just bring some of the stuff home and do it one evening?'

'Yeah, but that would be stealing, Mum.' Marilyn caught her father's eye in the rear-view mirror and they winked at one another.

'No it's not, it's homework. Can't do your homework without materials. Besides, it's family, it doesn't count.' Douggie's logic never let him down.

'I think what I really need is to start all over again. I've been doing my make-up the same for years, I could do with a change. I don't know what suits me any more. It's all right at your age, everything looks good; now I just look like mutton when I tart up.' Rita licked a finger and smoothed her eyebrows.

'That's because you should be wearing less make-up as you get older, Mum, not more. Most colours are really ageing, you need some nice neutral shades and forget the eyeliner, it just shows up the lines.'

'Yeah, well I've got plenty of them.'

Rita turned to look at her husband when they passed the Reading exit. 'Weren't we supposed to get off there?'

'No, I thought I'd go up to junction 12, take the Pangbourne Road and cut round the back, following the river.'

'You always have to go round the houses, don't you? Why can't you just go the easiest way?'

'You don't see anything that way. It'll be nice.'

'Oh come on, Dad, we've been in this bloody car for two

hours, my arse has gone numb.' Ronnie spoke his first words since the journey began. Apart from changing the cassettes in his Walkman, his only activities had been unwrapping sweets to put in his mouth and playing with the electric windows. His sister looked at him in surprise.

'Who rattled your cage?' she said.

'Shut up, you slag.'

'Don't speak to your sister like that.' Rita turned round and waved a warning finger at her son.

'He's pissed off because he's got so many spots,' said Marilyn. Rita gave up and let them bicker it out in the back; they'd be there in a minute and then they'd have to behave themselves.

'Are you sure we're going the right way, Doug?' As she spoke they passed a sign that said: SONNING 2 MILES. 'Sorry, I'll shut up.'

'Get that piece of paper out of my jacket with the directions on please, love.' Douggie held his hand out, then, steering with his elbows while he read, spoke quietly to himself: ' "Pass French Horn restaurant on the left, carry on over the bridge then as the road curves round to the right you'll see the brick wall surrounding the house. Park opposite and come in through door in wall." Sounds like a prison.'

They slowed as they crossed the river, looking out for the house. The houses they passed were white- and cream-walled and brick, decorated with clematis and honeysuckle about to bloom. Though modest in size, their well-tended exteriors and cultivated gardens screamed money.

'That's it,' Rita said.

'How do you know?' Douggie asked.

'Because I've seen pictures of it in a book in the library.'

'You didn't tell me.'

'What does it matter? That's it, pull over.'

Rita stepped out of the car when they'd parked and said, 'Doesn't look like much from the outside. A brick wall right on the main road.'

Douggie and Ronnie unloaded the bags while Marilyn pulled down her skirt, smoothing out the creases from the journey. Rita pinched the end off her lit cigarette and put the stub back in the packet, saving it for later. As they stood on the other side of the road, waiting for the traffic to pass, the wooden door in the wall opened and Frank Skinner came through it. Dressed in golfing trousers and a yellow jersey, he was the picture of relaxed middle-aged affluence. He looked very fit and like he'd had a bit of sun. Rita pulled her stomach in. Frank stared at her as they all crossed the road, but extended his hand to Doug first.

'Nice to see you all.' He nodded at Rita and the children, who mumbled their hellos, then he said, 'Right, come in and let's get you all a drink.'

The Fishers were taken aback by the layout of a house that couldn't be judged from the first few steps into the hallway. It seemed that doors led to corridors which led to rooms which fed back into other corridors. It wasn't so much the size, though the sheer scale was like nothing they'd ever seen before, but the complexity of its design. Built in 1900, Deanery Gardens was one of Lutyens's first romantic country houses, the main room flooded with light from the floor-to-ceiling leaded windows. The exceptionally high-ceilinged room incorporated an orchestra balcony, grand hearth and low-lying coffee table almost the size of Ronnie's bedroom. Douggie raved, 'Beautiful drum, eh Rita?' while the children were mute, cowed by a wealth they'd seen only in American soap operas. Rita perched on the edge of an oversized sofa saying little and staring curiously at the abstract paintings around the room. She noticed the lamps and cigarette boxes, the upholstery of the furniture and the huge vase filled with tropical flowers which sat in front of the fireguard. Rita knew it cost a bomb to get those kind of blooms this early in the year.

Doreen walked into the lounge and kissed Rita hello. 'I expect you'd like some tea. There's some champagne chilling, but we don't like to drink before five,' she said. All eyes flew to the clock above the fireplace: 4.20 p.m.

'You've got some lovely bits and pieces,' Rita said. Doreen beamed triumphantly. 'Mostly Arts & Crafts.' Rita smiled and nodded; she never went near arts and crafts herself, preferring a decent shop like Allders for her knick-knacks and ornaments.

Doreen tried to make conversation with Marilyn and Ronnie of the 'how-are-you-getting-on-at-school?' variety and Rita was shocked at the politeness of their replies. She had a stab of maternal sympathy – if she felt out of her depth, God knows what the kids must be thinking. But she was re-assured to see Ronnie confidently stretch his lanky legs and put his feet up on the coffee table. Doreen looked on in mild horror, studying the soles of his trainers for mud. That's my boy, Rita thought.

When the teacups had been cleared away Frank produced an ice-bucket with a magnum of champagne and seven glasses, explaining that the seventh glass was for their son Mark, due any time now from London – 'I thought, seeing as you'll be working closely with Mark at the club, you should have a chat this weekend. You'll be jointly in charge.' Douggie digested this information uncomfortably. Mark? He could remember the old days when the children were young, taking Mark swimming with Steven and clipping him round the ear when he got a bit boisterous. He wasn't sure about this new arrangement. All right, Mark was a grown man now, twenty-four, but surely the whole point of this new arrangement was that he was supposed to be Frank's partner?

'Won't you be at the club then, Frank?'

'Of course, Doug, of course,' Frank reassured him. 'It's just that I have to travel so much I need a good deputy.'

'Well you won't need me as well then, will you?'

'Bloody hard work managing a club you know, Doug, you can't do six days a week on your own. Someone's got to be there during the day to check in all the deliveries, and then there's the late nights. You'd kill yourself trying to do it all alone.' Frank handed Rita a glass of champagne which she took, avoiding his eye. Then he served Marilyn, Doreen, Ronnie, who burst out, 'Oh the pink stuff, nice one! I had this at Spencer's last Christmas', and finally Doug, who for now set aside his worries about heartburn.

'If there's that much to be done maybe I should get my Steven to help out as well,' Douggie challenged Frank. Rita shot him a warning look.

'Whatever you think, Doug. But let's not talk about business now. Here's to a great weekend.' He raised his glass: 'Health and unity, dark corners and opportunity.'

Rita's heart went out to her husband; Frank was doing it again, the bastard. Unable to sit there and watch Doug be humiliated, she expressed interest in the garden. Maybe Doreen could show her around? 'Of course, but first I'll show you to your rooms, I'm sure you'll want to freshen up.'

Marilyn was delighted to find that her room had a double bed and en-suite bathroom. It was set in a little recess away from the other rooms so she figured she could skin up and nobody would know. She hastily unpacked her cosmetics and toiletries and excused herself from the garden tour on the pretext that she wanted to have a long soak and condition her hair. Ronnie went with his father and Frank to the snooker room for a few frames and Rita followed Doreen out of the kitchen door.

Her shoes sank into the soft ground as they walked and she tried to lean forward on the balls of her feet to avoid staining the suede heels. She noted Doreen's stout gardening shoes and suddenly felt stupid for coming to the country with inappropriate footwear. Now that she was in her hostess's home the differences between them seemed cruelly marked.

Doreen was a country woman now: a velvet hairband kept her thinning platinum hair out of her eyes and her padded bodywarmer left her arms free to point while Rita's were busy hugging her angora sweater more tightly to her. Doreen explained that on Sunday, after lunch, it was traditional for the children in the village to come to Deanery Gardens for an Easter-egg hunt. 'What, they have to wait until Sunday to get their eggs? Poor little sods. My lot would do their nut.' Doreen smiled patiently at Rita, who blushed as her gaffe dawned upon her.

There were about four acres of grounds in all, which, Doreen explained, wasn't very much for a house of this size and period, especially compared to some of the other piles in the area. After three-quarters of an hour, Rita thought it was quite big enough. Her feet were soaked through and she still hadn't seen the kitchen garden. She made appreciative noises, but thought to herself that she couldn't stand anything this big, gardeners or not. There was something impersonal about it, it was too immaculate. It didn't look like somewhere you could actually live. Almost out of the blue, Rita couldn't resist asking, 'Are you happy here, Doreen?'

'Yes, of course, why shouldn't I be?'

Marilyn loved her room: she decided that when she left home she would look for a bedroom with an en-suite bathroom – you could lay all your bits out and nobody could tell you to tidy them up. She lounged in the bath with *Hair and Beauty* magazine and a joint while a deep-conditioning pack penetrated her highlighted hair, trying to restore some natural shine. While she was lying there, a great idea for shading the face to achieve a natural look came to her. She stepped out of the bath, pulled one of the enormous fluffy bathsheets around her and rifled her bag for a pencil. She couldn't find any paper in the room, so perched dripping at the desk and sketched directly on to the ink blotter. She drew a crude face, then imposed a grid on it and with arrows devised an exact shading system that started level with the bottom of the ears. 'Yes, yes!' she cried excitedly and in her large looped writing, wrote in block capitals 'NO MAKE-UP MAKE-UP' at the top of the blotter.

She stopped short, suddenly remembering the burning joint. When she went back into the bathroom, she saw that it had rolled out of the ashtray she had fashioned from the lid of her can of hairspray and was now on the pale lilac carpet, where it had burned a sizeable hole. She rubbed and rubbed at it with a flannel and in the end decided just to move the bath mat to cover her crime and go back to the desk and finish her sketching. She could see the exact colour she would use – a kind of pink-beige. Her mind raced ahead to the day when she would have her own line of cosmetics. This course was the best thing she had ever done. She'd made some great mates already just from the induction day and was surprised to find that most of them weren't the least bit like Shelley. Just regular girls that wanted to learn a trade, earn a few bob and liked a laugh. After drying her hair, painting her nails and carefully dressing, she grabbed the blotting paper to take downstairs and show to her dad.

She found him in the snooker room with Ronnie, Frank and his son Mark. It was years since she'd seen Mark; he'd been an ungainly youth and she'd been a plump unpromising little girl. In the intervening years, they'd both changed a great deal and their eyes locked for an instant, both pleasantly surprised. They exchanged hellos and though their kiss of greeting was chaste, Marilyn felt a spark. Mark was tall and broad and when he bent over the table to take a shot, she appraised his backside. Suddenly she felt overcome by shyness and ill at ease in the manly atmosphere of the room. Cigar smoke hung heavy, lit by an early evening sun streaming through the windows. They had finished the champagne and moved on to cans of beer. From the jibes and loud pitch of their voices she could tell they were half-cut. She hoped none of them had noticed her stoned and glassy eyes.

'All right baby, d'ya have a nice bath?' Noting her discomfort, Douggie clasped a protective arm around her shoulder. 'What's that you've got in your hand?'

'Oh, it's nothing. Where's Mum?'

'Having a lie-down before dinner. Let's have a look at your piece of paper.'

'It's your shot, Doug,' said Frank. Doug moved unsteadily around the table and Marilyn found herself standing next to Mark, who openly sized her up and down as he chalked his cue. Soft and inviting, hers was a body that cried out to be ravished. Marilyn felt herself blushing and exited the room quickly, saying, 'I'll catch you later, Dad, I'm going to see Mum.'

As was her custom, Marilyn barged into her mother's room without knocking. Rita turned over, saw her and said, 'What's wrong, love?'

'Nothing, I just wanted to show you my drawing – I've had a brilliant idea for making up the whole face, just using one shade.'

Rita slumped back on her pillows with relief and smiled. 'Thank Christ for that, I thought there'd been a murder the way you came charging in.' Marilyn made an apologetic face, but her mother just said, 'It's all right sweetheart, I was just going to get up and have a bath anyway. What's the time?' She reached for her watch on the nightstand. 'Blimey, seven o'clock already, I've been out for almost an hour. What's your father up to?'

'Playing snooker with Frank and Ronnie.' She paused. 'And Mark,' she added.

'Oh, Mark's here. I haven't seen him for years. What's he like?'

'Nice.'

Rita looked at her daughter's face and said, 'Oh yeah, how nice?'

Marilyn laughed coyly, 'Shut up, Mum.'

'Yeah, yeah, all right, I won't grass you. I hope he's a bit nicer than his father. Don't fancy giving me a quick manicure do you, love?'

'Yeah, but I'm not going to paint them that bloody awful coral pink you use. You can have scarlet or a French manicure. What do you mean you hope he's nicer than his father?'

'Oh don't take any notice of me, I've just woken up with the 'ump. Look at the expert,' Rita said proudly as Marilyn picked up her hand and studied it and tutted at the uneven state of her nails. She'd really come on since deciding to go to college, and though Rita didn't like to get her hopes up, she had a feeling that her wayward daughter might finally have found her calling. Her moods seemed to have evened out a little and even though they hadn't got to meet this Nelson character yet, Rita thought he must be having a good effect on her.

'So what's this idea you've got for make-up, then?'

Marilyn unfolded her sketch and talked her mum through it. Sounded a bit weird to Rita, doing the whole face, eyes and all, in a pink colour, but she agreed to be her guinea-pig when Marilyn emphasised that such a shading scheme was perfect for a more 'mature' complexion. 'Not tonight though eh love, wait till we get home. Doreen said dinner's at 7.30 for eight. Whatever that means.'

When Marilyn finished her manicure, Rita washed her face, applied fresh make-up and perfume and ran a comb through her hair. Coming out of her bedroom she had the choice of two staircases: the wide central one that led into the main lobby or a smaller, recessed staircase at the back of the house. She decided to take the smaller one and see where it led. At the bottom was a chilly, narrow corridor with flagstones and several doors leading off it. She poked her head around each door, finding larders and utility rooms. She figured this part of the house must in some way be connected to the kitchen which it serviced.

From the far end of the corridor she could hear a muffled voice and inched towards it quietly; drawing closer she could see a shaft of light coming through a door not quite closed. It was definitely Frank's voice on the telephone but she stopped listening when something more interesting caught her eye. About five feet before the door on the same side was a glass-fronted gun cupboard where five shotguns hung. It wasn't unusual to find such a feature in a country house, except she couldn't really imagine Frank as the hunting type. His loud laugh startled her and she leaned closer to the door to listen.

'I'm back in the Dam next week so I'll confirm the dates when I see you then, but it's all looking sweet. Yeah, yeah, he's as good as gold, hasn't got a danny.' He laughed loudly again. 'Well, wouldn't want to worry him.'

He was talking about Douggie, she just knew it.

'Look, I'd better go, we've got people here for dinner. Yeah, yeah, later.'

Rita's heart pounded as she heard him put down the telephone. Quickly she retraced her steps on the balls of her feet to keep her heels from making a sound.

The oak-panelled dining room was about the loveliest thing Rita had ever seen. A fire blazed in the massive hearth over which hung an old gilt mirror with bits of the glass worn away. The room had a slightly tatty feel at odds with the rest of the immaculate house, but when the overhead candelabra was lit and the flames cast a warm glow around the room, bouncing the light off the crystal, Rita felt like she was at some posh do, and was glad she'd put her diamond earrings on.

Each place setting had three glasses and the wine had been decanted into what looked like large specimen bottles. The silverware was not in fact silver, but gold-plated. Rita thought it looked brassy, the kind of thing you'd expect an Arab to have, but Douggie was enthralled with it all and pronounced his joy loudly. He was in that pissed state where he loved everything and Rita just hoped he didn't pass out over dinner. Ronnie, unaccustomed to drinking all day, sat at the table looking dazed, his hands barely holding his head aloft. 'Get your elbows off the table and sit up straight,' Rita hissed across at him. Marilyn was seated between Ronnie and Mark, and Rita noticed how she ate, all ladylike, putting her knife and fork down between mouthfuls and taking tiny sips of her wine. Usually in the Fisher house, the business of eating and drinking was a competitive sport, a race to see who could be the first to bag the leftovers and grab another glass before the wine bottle was empty.

The food was sensational, pâté de foie gras followed by fresh tomato soup and then venison. It was foreign food to the Fishers but they wolfed it down with gusto. Rita was surprised to find how much she liked the rich, gamey meat, and the red wine, a Pinot Noir according to Frank, was like nothing she'd ever tasted. Seated next to Frank, who was poised like a monarch in the big chair with arms at the head of the table, Rita could hardly avoid speaking to him, and though she kept her answers brief but polite to start with, he showed such an interest in her, the shop, the children, her late mother – he even remembered Flossie – that after a couple of glasses of wine she found herself laughing easily.

At the other end of the table, Douggie was getting a bit touchy-feely with the hostess, but Doreen seemed to be laughing along with him, so Rita didn't bother herself unduly. Only once – when she heard him start his joke 'What do you call a black woman that has an abortion?' – did she leap in before the punchline and ask Doreen where she bought her meat. Marilyn and Mark were absorbed in each other and Rita smiled at the gentlemanly way he refilled her glass and lit her cigarettes for her. Ronnie had to apply all his concentration just to get his food in his mouth, so there was nothing for it but to enjoy Frank's attention.

He spoke of the days when he used to hang about with her brother Neville and what a laugh they had teasing her first boyfriend – 'What was his name, wimpy bloke with glasses that ended up going to university? Total knob.'

'He was not, he was lovely, he just wasn't rough like the rest of you. Dickie French. Moved to Australia in the sixties, he was an engineer, did well for himself.'

'Dickie French, that was him,' Frank laughed. 'And you could have had your pick.'

'Oh don't be daft.' Rita coloured shyly. 'I was tubby.'

'You were gorgeous. Still are.' Rita let him fill her glass while she steeled herself.

'So then Frank, do you get involved in country things?'

'Like what?'

'Oh, I don't know . . . horse-riding, hunting, shooting birds, that sort of thing.'

'No, not me, I'm too busy. Besides, I can't stand the people. It's good to have the peace and quiet at weekends, but mostly I like to be in town.' He leaned in closer. 'It'll be good to see more of you again when we get this club off the ground, Rita. It'll be like the old days.'

'That's just what I was thinking.'

CHAPTER SIX

Old Dogs, New Tricks

Douggie drew the Mercedes level with the kerb hastily, clipping a motorbike parked at a rakish angle outside the Poland Club; it rocked for a second or two then stabilised in the upright position, but not before its owner had witnessed the brush of metal. Douggie switched off his engine and climbed out of the car to find the motorcycle messenger furiously examining his rear mudguard for signs of damage. Another time and Douggie would have turned on the charm and offered sincere apologies but he was so uptight he merely glared.

'For fuck's sake,' the courier hissed.

'Want to make something of it?'

The messenger relaxed his stance a little. 'Well you did just knock my bike, mate.'

'Lucky I didn't write it off, the way you parked it.' No stranger to these daily skirmishes in the central zone, the courier muttered something unsavoury under his breath, fastened his helmet and started the engine.

Douggie was in a foul mood. Despite the beautiful spring evening boosted by the recent change to Summer Time and the fact that his first night at the club should be the cause for some excitement, his lady wife had put him in a gloomy state. He'd popped in to see her at the shop just as she was closing, to get her approval on his appearance and a good-will kiss. 'Aren't you going to wish me luck?' he asked, and she'd fixed him with one of her finest withering looks. 'Reckon you'll need it. Personally, I'd have just taken the twenty grand out of the bank and set fire to it.' He preferred her angry to sarcastic. She had a wicked tongue in her head and wasn't afraid to use it. She could be a right bitch sometimes, Rita.

He thought she'd finally come round to the idea after a good weekend in Sonning, but as early as the journey back to Purley on Easter Monday she'd adopted the silent routine, opening her mouth only to put the dampeners on Douggie's enthusiasm: 'It's got pear-shaped written all over it.' That she was outnumbered at home wasn't helping. Steve and Marilyn were behind their father, though Ronnie was indifferent – not averse to taking the piss out of his dad, but secretly quite pleased to be able to swank about 'their club' at school. Douggie figured, a little too optimistically, that if he could win round the kids, Rita would finally soften, but isolation had fixed her resolve and she wouldn't budge. Her pinched frostiness and silence at mealtimes was getting to him.

'I'll be glad of somewhere to go of an evening if this is what I've got to come home to,' he'd said. But she could be fantastically stubborn and merely lifted her eyebrows in a 'see if I care' manner.

Douggie's collar felt tight and he undid the top button and loosened his tie before walking through the door of the club. His affected swagger did little to impress the receptionist, who simply looked up from her copy of the *Standard* and stared at him by way of enquiry.

'Is Mark here, love?' he asked.

'Inside. And my name's Amanda, not love.'

Douggie bumbled an apology then, amazed to find himself saying sorry to someone who was now a member of his staff, bit the inside of his cheek with anger. He found Mark standing with two white-shirted men behind the bar and introductions were made. Both barmen were Australian and seemed friendly. Mark explained the system.

'The bar staff come in at six to stock up during the week, about seven o'clock on Saturday because we open later. You need to check the rota downstairs to see who's on and all the numbers are in the book in case any of them are late or call in sick. Usually we have a couple of girls on the floor taking orders, but a lot of the business is over the bar.'

Acid rose in Douggie's stomach and he remembered he hadn't eaten since that morning. 'Any grub?' he asked.

'Yeah, we do a small bar menu.' Mark handed him a plastic card with the limited food options. 'Nothing special, you know, just potato skins, burgers, spare ribs, stuff that can be knocked up quickly. It means if the chef doesn't turn up for any reason, it's not too difficult for one of us to take over. Food's not available till nine.'

'I was thinking more of me.' Douggie shuffled, feeling a bit stupid, but Mark put him at his ease. 'Yeah, course, come on. I'll show you the kitchen. Chicken and chips?'

'Beautiful. Cheers, Mark.'

They walked out the back and Douggie thought he saw one of the barmen say something to the other and laugh. When he looked back they were staring straight at him. Mark said, 'Don't worry, Doug, it seems like a lot to take in at first, but you'll pick it up in no time. Just remember not to take any shit from the staff. Start as you mean to go on. They're not a bad bunch, but they're like anyone else, if they think they can take the piss and get away with it, they will.'

Mark opened one of the tall fridges and pulled out a chicken breast, showing Douggie how the meats had to be kept separate from the other foods. Health and safety regulations.

'Who's that bird on the desk?' Douggie asked.

'Oh Amanda. She's an actress. Thinks she's too good for us.'

'Why don't you get shot of her, then?'

'Well, you can if you like, Doug. You're a partner now.

The old man thinks she looks good on the desk though. You know what he's like for a bit of posh.'

Douggie had warmed a lot to Mark over the weekend at Sonning. Found him a nice kid, straightforward, friendly. Rita said she thought Mark and Marilyn had got on very well that weekend, but Douggie hadn't noticed anything, even Marilyn getting up to go and spray on more perfume every ten minutes. After his initial disappointment, he was coming round to the idea of working with Mark. It wasn't as if he was trying to tell him what to do and he had even said it was fine by him if Doug wanted to bring Steve in to help out for a couple of shifts. He did point out, though, that Steve's wages would have to come out of Douggie's share of the profits, once all the bills had been paid. But that seemed fair enough. As it turned out, Steve had had to go to court to get the licence to sell alcohol. The previous licensee had been the manager Frank had sacked when he'd finally caught him with his hand in the till. As Doug, Frank and Mark were unable to apply for a licence because of previous convictions, Steve slotted in naturally. As long as Doug didn't mind Steve not being on the payroll officially, Mark reckoned it was 'no skin off my nose'.

Full up with chicken and chips and a beer, Douggie felt much better and found himself really concentrating when Mark took him down to the office next to the loos and ran through the procedures – all the stock books, where deliveries were written down, addresses of their suppliers, the staff rota and address book, list of useful numbers on the wall, especially the alarm company who Mark said Doug would be dealing with a lot, as the poxy thing kept going off at all hours.

'On Thursdays the bookkeeper comes in to do the wages. She's a nice old bird, no trouble, but you have to have the wages sheets ready for her with all the hours down. She's very by the book and wants everybody's P45. We still pay the staff in cash, but all the deductions come out first, so it's kosher. We're thinking of doing that thing where you pay direct into their bank accounts, but it's hardly worth it in this game, with the staff turnover. A lot of them left when we booted the old manager, but only because we rumbled their fiddle. What they'd do was Z-off the till reading about an hour before we closed and then pocket the rest of the night's takings.'

Douggie looked perplexed.

'What it is, Doug, you've got your X reading and your Z reading: your X reading gives you your takings to date, so you can check it throughout the day, and the Z reading gives you the totals. Once you've taken the Z, the till's memory wipes clean and there's no comeback.' Mark laughed at Douggie's expression. 'Honestly, Doug, it sounds complicated, but it's pretty easy. I only started about six weeks ago when we sacked the other bloke and now I feel like I've been here for donkey's years. Right then, here's your set of keys.'

Douggie felt the weight of the large bunch. He paid close attention while Mark talked him through it: safe keys, stock cupboard keys, fridge keys, alarm keys, till keys, door keys, locker keys. He hooked the large ring on to his belt loop and immediately felt more confident. Nothing like a big bunch of keys to make you feel important.

Douggie was whistling when he went up the stairs. He paused for a minute at the top and looked at Amanda through the glass portholes in the door that separated the bar from reception. She was gassing away on the phone, laughing. Didn't sound like a business call. As she chatted she leafed through a glossy magazine and fixed her make-up in a mirror she had propped up on the desk. 'Right, lady, I've got your number,' Douggie whispered to himself.

At the bar, two waitresses were wrapping white aprons around their waists and chatting to the barmen. Douggie sauntered over, and asked one of them for another beer. When the girls fixed him with quizzical looks, he introduced himself as their new boss. At this they quickly apologised for smoking, but Doug just said, 'Don't worry, girls, finish your fags, we're not open yet.' The two girls, Sally and an Irish girl called Eimar, pulled pleased faces at each other, then Eimar resumed her story: 'So I sez to him, right, you're a fuckin' eejit, I wouldn't go out with you if you paid me.'

Douggie looked at her laughing face and winked. He liked her. She had a bit of sparkle. He could tell already, she was going to be his little mate. When Douggie started flipping through the tapes and pulled out a collection of jazz hits, Eimar jumped in. 'Oh, Jesus! Not that one, you'll put us all to sleep.' She shoved him to one side and picked out another tape, 'D'ya dance the samba, Douggie?' When he replied he was more of a jive man, she shrieked with laughter. 'God Almighty, you and me father. C'mon I'll show yez.' She grabbed Douggie by the hands and started to show him steps. 'Honestly, you're as stiff as a board.'

'In all the right places.' Douggie was feeling bold.

'Get away with ye, ye maniac.' As they attempted their steps, Amanda strolled into the bar. She stared incredulously at the unfolding scene.

'Have ye met the new boss man, Amanda? He's a riot!'

'Pleased to meet you,' Amanda said frostily, before strutting away and calling back in a schoolmarmish tone, 'You might like to know that we are open now.'

Eimar looked at Douggie's hurt expression and said, 'Ah take no notice of her, stuck-up little cow, she needs a good kick up the arse. I swear to God, I've never seen the woman crack a smile.'

Supposedly a members' club, the Poland would in fact let a coachload in as long as there was one member amongst them. In most such clubs the number of guests was kept strictly to four, but the Poland didn't do such great business if they enforced the rules too strictly. The management had developed an ad hoc system of letting in friends, friends of friends, business associates and anybody who looked like they wouldn't wreck the joint. Non-members were asked to pay a £5 entry fee, but even this could be circumvented by a nod from the doorman.

By nine o'clock Douggie had already drunk four beers and was feeling at a loss what to do with himself. Mark settled in at a table with a group of friends and was polite enough to invite Douggie to join them for a drink, but he felt out of place and had nothing much to say. He managed for a while with football, but when the conversation turned to clubs and women, he felt like an old man and wandered outside to talk to the doormen. Brian, the bouncer he'd met that first evening he'd visited with Rita, was extremely welcoming to Douggie and talked him through the guests as they trickled in. The crowd consisted mostly of restaurant and club owners in the Soho area who would come to the Poland for a warm-up drink before heading off home or on to clubs with later licences. Because the Poland only had a 1 a.m. licence, it didn't really work as a place for raves, Brian explained.

Douggie was relieved: he fancied neither the late nights, nor the prospect of having to dance with a bunch of kids. After an hour on the door, he wandered back inside to the bar. It was still only 10.30. He looked at his watch every ten minutes or so and at one point even wished that Rita was there.

He took up position at the end of the bar with Mark, who told him that this was the best place to keep an eye on what went in and out of the tills. Douggie noticed that Mark wasn't drinking and when he quizzed him on it, Mark said that he didn't like to drink when he was working as it made him feel tired and he needed to be on the ball. Besides, it set a bad example to the staff, who would think it was all right for them to help themselves. Douggie felt embarrassed, his fifth beer of the evening clutched in his paw. Mark said, 'Don't worry, Doug, it's your first night, you're bound to feel like a bit of a lemon, but go easy on the beer – you don't want to get a tug on the way home.'

By some kind of auto-reflex Douggie started pouring fist-fuls of peanuts down his throat as if to soak up the liquor, but that just made him more thirsty, and the next time Mark went to the toilet, which seemed to be every five minutes, Douggie motioned to the barman for another.

By 11.30 the Poland Club was at full capacity. All the tables were occupied and the crowd at the bar was pretty thick. Douggie asked the barmen if they wanted any help and Greg, a tall Australian, replied, 'Yeah, but can you make a drink?'

'Well I can open bottles of beer if that's what you mean?'

'I was thinking more of cocktails.'

'I can have a go.'

'Sure, if you like.'

He folded his jacket up, placing it on a shelf behind the bar, and rolled up his sleeves. Smiling broadly at his first cus-tomer, a young woman with dyed black hair and a short skirt, he said, 'What can I get you, love?' She wanted two white wines. Douggie's relief was evident. He poured two glasses and then when she looked at him, remembered that he didn't know what anything cost. The barman shouted, '£2.50 each' and Douggie triumphantly took the fiver from her hands then realised that he didn't know how to work the till either. He stood there looking perplexed while the other two barmen waited patiently behind him with money that they wanted to key in. Greg showed him how it worked, but Douggie felt he really wanted it explained again. He took a few more orders which were, thankfully, simple, but found himself getting under the barmen's feet and generally feeling like a hindrance.

Mark came back from the toilets, sniffed loudly and laughed good-naturedly. 'Getting stuck in then, Doug?'

'Getting in the way more like. 'This small acknowledgement endeared him to Greg.

'I tell you what, Douggie,' he said. 'No worries tonight eh, just enjoy yourself, but if you like I can show you how it works another night. Come in an hour early or something.'

'Yeah that would be great, mate. Cheers.' Exhausted from his ten-minute stint, Douggie pulled another Becks out of the fridge and retired to the end of the bar with Mark, who seemed fidgety, bouncing his foot up and down on the bar rail. 'You got St Vitus dance or something?' Douggie asked. Mark just smiled and turned to greet a short man with a thick neck: 'Gerry, what's up? Meet Douggie Fisher, Dad's new partner. Gerry Solano, owns the Genoa Café round the corner, one of our best members.'

Douggie and the man with the thick neck pumped hands and looked at each other, some faint recognition playing on their faces. 'Not Bert Fisher's brother?' he asked, his hand still gripping Douggie's.

'Yeah, you know my Bert?'

'We did our National Service together in Nottingham,' said the thick neck, breaking into a wide grin.

'No,' gawped Douggie open-mouthed. 'Not Genoa Gerry! It can't be.'

'The very same,' Genoa Gerry answered with pride. 'I still remember you in short trousers when we used to come round your mum's with a weekend pass. How is Olive?'

'Oh Mum, she passed away five years ago. Cancer got her.'

'I'm so sorry to hear that. I liked your mum, quite a tough old bird I remember. She used to go dancing up the Locarno in Streatham High Road. She can't have been that old, Doug?'

'No, only fifty-eight. Mind you, she did smoke a hundred

a day. Like the bloody wife. I'm always getting on at her to pack 'em in, she lost her mum two years ago. Same thing.'

'You're married then, got a family?'

'Yeah, three kids, bloody useless the lot of 'em!'

Both men roared loudly at this. Parental pride in South London was often best demonstrated by putting the kids down. Douggie motioned to the barman for more drinks, marking the happy occasion by moving on to Scotch and Coke.

'Do you·remember Neville Curtis?' Doug asked. Gerry nodded, swallowing a big draught of Scotch. 'Well,' Douggie went on, 'I married his sister.'

'No? Last I heard she was courting Frank, I wondered what had happened to her. Obviously she didn't marry him, because he took up with Doreen Pearce, but I had no idea. Goes quick, don't it.'

'Yeah, don't it. Anyway what you up to these days?'

'Just the place round the corner. Makes a fortune because we're open through the night. I don't have a lot to do with it these days, I let my boys get on with it.'

'Where are you living now, then?'

'Mill Hill. Nice, got some good properties. We left Lewisham in '72 because the schools were so shit, you know, no green for the kids to knock a ball about.'

Meanwhile, in reception, an altogether less cordial exchange was in hand.

'I'm afraid it's members only.' Amanda surveyed Marilyn's suburban style with distaste: the square shoulders of her jacket and the cut of the skirt, too short for somebody with Marilyn's thighs, and the stockings too sheer, showing every fold of flesh hanging over the knees. As for the voice . . .

'I'm here to see me dad.' Marilyn had one hand on hip, a tough stance that didn't match her feelings. Girls who spoke nicely always made her feel stupid and the fact that Amanda was wearing a simple shift dress and a small pair of earrings made Marilyn feel weighted down with gold. Perhaps she had overdone it – belcher chain, gate bracelet, both of her sovereigns. Only her thumbs were unadorned by rings.

'I don't appear to have your name on the list.'

'I can see him from here.' Marilyn pointed through the glass porthole. 'Why can't I just go in?' Giving Amanda's face a closer inspection, Marilyn was pleased to see that under her foundation she had terrible skin – all bumps and open pores. If there was one thing about Marilyn that was flawless, it was her complexion. She started to feel better.

'I'll go and have a word. Please take a seat.'

Marilyn flopped down heavily into one of the deep leather chairs and looked around the reception. Not bad. Wood panels, chesterfield sofas, carpet had a few fag burns, but altogether, quite, quite all right. The door swung open heavily and Douggie's beaming face appeared.

'Dewdrop! What you doing in the West End this time of night?'

'I was out with the girls from college having a drink and I just thought I'd jump on the train at East Croydon. Only took twenty minutes.'

'Does your mother know where you are? She'll be worried.'

'Yeah, I rang up from the station.'

'You're not pissed, are you?'

'No.'

'Good, you can drive your old man home. Come on, come in.'

Walking into the bar, Marilyn glanced back over her shoulder and shot Amanda a dirty look. Douggie walked Marilyn over to the end of the bar with a protective arm around her shoulders, squeezing her affectionately. 'Glad you're here, love, I could do with a bit of moral. Felt like a spare part tonight – Gerry, this is my daughter Marilyn.'

Gerry shook her hand and looked at her approvingly.

'Dead spit of her mother, Doug.'

'Yeah, ain't she? Bloody handful as well.' Marilyn smiled sweetly, distractedly searching the club until her gaze alighted on the figure she was searching for. When she caught his eye, he did a double-take, smiled broadly and walked over.

'Hello Mark.'

'All right?' They stood awkwardly for a few moments. 'Come to check up on your dad, then?' he said.

'Yeah, thought he might want a bit of company on his first night. Poor old Dad, everybody's getting on his case indoors. Well, Mum is.'

'That's what mums are for. Can I get you a drink?'

'Yeah, I better just have a Coke. Dad looks like he won't be able to drive. Where are the loos?' Marilyn sniffed.

'Oh, right. Yeah come on, I'll show you.'

Douggie and Gerry watched them walk towards the staircase that led to the basement. Gerry gave Douggie a nudge. 'Watch out, Doug, looks like something's up with those two.'

'That's what Rita reckons, but Marilyn's already got a boyfriend, supposedly, not that we've ever met him.'

'They chop and change every five minutes, these kids. Not like in our day, you met a girl, took her out and if you wanted a bit of the other you had to get married.'

Douggie leaned on the bar and considered this, waving his glass at Greg for refills. 'I don't understand it. They've got more freedom, but it doesn't seem to help them when they do get married. They're divorced five minutes later or having affairs. Take me and Reet, we've had our ups and downs but I'd never have an affair and neither would she.'

Gerry looked at Doug sideways. 'Different values, Doug.' He offered a £20 note to the barman. 'I'll get these. I mean, look at my two boys, different bird every five minutes. Louie's thirty-two now and he's still not settled. I've told him, he'll be past it once he does get round to having kids. They're all doing it so much later now, there's going to be a whole generation of them not having kids till they're in their late thirties. Too late if you ask me. They'll be old men by the time their kids have grown up.'

Marilyn and Mark came back up the stairs as the lights were going up and last orders had been called. People started to drift out and the staff were moving quickly to get the glasses cleared.

'Dad, Mark says I can have a part-time job at weekends.'

'Fantastic. Save me a bit of dough.'

'Well, we don't have any gaps at the moment,' cautioned Mark, 'but I think Sally's planning to go off travelling this summer, so you can always take her four shifts if you like.'

Douggie breathed deeply with a sense of well-being. The first night hadn't gone too bad in the finish. Bumping into Gerry was a turn-up for the books and now he'd have his two eldest children on hand at the club. Rita was going to have to buck her ideas up.

'Come on, Doug, I'm going to cash off the tills, you'll have to pay attention. The first thing we do is start counting the change and work up to £200. That's our float, everything after that comes out and we count it and balance it against the readings. The float goes in the red bag and then in the safe downstairs. The rest goes in the yellow bags for the bank in the morning. If you can count the money for me, I'll do the readings.'

One thing Douggie could do in any condition was count money and he set about it with the precision of a bank clerk. When they came back from the office, after Mark had shown Douggie the safe combination and the locking-up procedure, they found Marilyn and the two waitresses at the bar having their staff drinks while waiting for their cabs to arrive.

'Well done, girls, good work,' Douggie called.

'We never did get our dance, Douggie. I'll just have to dream about it,' said Eimar.

'I can see I'm going to have to watch you. You're a little raver.'

'You bet yer life I am,' Eimar said. 'Say now, Mark, I want to go back to Cork the weekend after next for me mother's birthday. Can I swap some shifts?'

'I'll do them for you,' Marilyn offered.

'Oh, you're an angel. Would you like a ciggie?'

'Cheers.'

A tall middle-aged man appeared in the doorway and stood staring until he caught Mark's eye. Mark jumped off his bar stool and disappeared down the stairs with the man. 'Who's that?' Doug asked.

'Come to get his hush money,' said Eimar before Greg silenced her with a look.

'What hush money?' The sudden quiet gave Doug an uneasy feeling and he had a flash of fear. He walked down the stairs and barged into the office to find Mark handing an envelope to the man, who slipped it into his inside pocket. 'What's going on?'

'Just a bit of personal business, Doug. John, this is Douggie Fisher, Dad's new partner. Doug, this is Detective Inspector John Carlisle. He's a friend of Dad's who helps us out.'

'Helps out with what?'

'Watches out for trouble.' The policeman shook Douggie's hand and slipped out, saying he'd be in touch.

'How come we're giving the Old Bill money? I thought this was legit.'

'It *is* legit, but John keeps an eye on things for us. Some people don't like Dad, and John lets us know who to watch for.'

'What do you mean some people don't like your dad?'

'Honestly Doug, it's nothing to worry about.'

'Why do we give them money, then? I'm fucked if I'm working nights to pay off a bent copper for something I don't even know about.'

'Look, I think you're better off speaking to Dad about it, Doug. But honestly, it just means we keep the Old Bill off our backs.'

'Yeah, but why do we need to?' Douggie's boozy *bonhomie* was developing an edge.

'Drugs, Douggie. Every club's got problems with drugs. Most of the punters in here tonight would have had something on them and it just means we don't get raided.'

'Oh great! Funny your old man never mentioned this.' Douggie ran a hand across his thinning hair.

'I think you'd better speak to him about it.'

Douggie pointed a finger at Mark. 'Don't worry, I will,' he said then stormed up the stairs, grabbed Marilyn's arm and said, 'Come on, we're going.'

'What's the matter, Dad?'

'Get your coat.'

CHAPTER SEVEN

The Rot Sets In

Douggie confronted Frank the following morning. He waited till he got to the car lot to make the call; he wasn't about to give Rita the satisfaction of bad news quite so soon.

Frank had his work cut out mollifying Douggie; he lunched him at Quo Vadis in Dean Street and asked the waiter to leave the bottle of Armagnac on the table afterwards. Douggie wasn't moved by Frank's efforts to persuade him that times had changed and that drugs were everywhere, a fact of life. 'I don't care, I haven't been in trouble with the law for years and I'm not about to start again now. For fuck's sake Frank I'm pushing fifty, I don't need the ag.'

Douggie would look back on this moment as a missed opportunity to cut his losses, but his pride was at stake. He was so determined to prove his wife wrong that he just put the blinkers on.

As the weeks went by, the Fishers adjusted to their new routine. Douggie settled in at the Poland, coming to an arrangement with Mark that he would work Tuesday and Wednesday evenings alone and together they would work the Saturday shift. The busiest evenings in the West End were Thursdays and Fridays, with Saturday drawing a more suburban crowd that Douggie felt at home with. Steve worked with his father on Tuesday and Wednesday evenings and Marilyn had managed to get two shifts a week, working Friday and Saturday evenings. Ronnie had been down a couple of times on a Saturday with his mates, but Mark said it made him uneasy to have under-age kids hanging about. 'Amount of money you give your mate I'm surprised you even get parking tickets,' Douggie had said. That soon shut him up.

The only member of the family not to have patronised the Poland since its new partner had arrived was Rita. It was the loneliest spring she could remember. The longer evenings meant she could do some work in the garden when she got home from the shop. But it wasn't the same if she couldn't hear all the televisions blaring indoors and the assorted voices of her family in dispute. She'd be planting the borders and stop, listening for a noise, but no sound could be heard. She'd given up cooking tea the nights Doug wasn't home; Ronnie would either be studying with sandwiches and the biscuit tin in his room or round at Spencer's. Marilyn often went out after college and if she came home at all, it wasn't till after Rita had turned in for the night. And Douggie – well, two nights a week he went straight from the car lot to the club and the nights he was at home he tended to fall asleep in his chair. The original plan had been to leave Steve in charge of the car lot, but Douggie was finding it harder than he expected to relinquish control, though he was the only member of the family to be surprised by this. It was clearly all a bit of a strain for him: even if he claimed to be having a good time, Rita sensed that he couldn't bear to lose face by admitting he had taken on too much. Had he been describing another man, Douggie would have said he'd 'dropped a bollock'.

The family member Rita saw most of was the one who no longer lived at home. Steve would often pop in for a cup of tea on his way home to Norwood to try and cheer his mother up, but couldn't tell her much without betraying his father. Douggie had managed to swear Marilyn and Steve to secrecy over the police bunging situation – 'Everyone does it, it's nothing to worry about, but best your mum doesn't find out eh? Wouldn't want to get her all worked up.' It was a strange state of affairs. Each family member kept their worries to themselves in their efforts not to worry anybody else. If they all put on a brave face and acted optimistically, each hoped things would sort themselves out. Douggie could no more afford to lose face than he could £20,000. His share of the profits from the club were respectable but in no way matched up to the fantasy figures posited in his initial discussions with Frank. Rita hadn't said, 'I told you so.' She didn't need to.

Rita grew lonely in the night. Just as it was with the children, so with Douggie – she couldn't fall asleep until she heard his footfall on the stairs. She hadn't felt this drained since Ronnie was a baby and up all night. Every night she half expected a phone call from the police station – that Doug hadn't been done for drink-driving was by the grace of God. He always said he wouldn't have a drink, but she knew that taking it easy for Doug usually involved five or six beers. He couldn't get away with it for ever; his luck would have to run out one day. 'What will you do then, eh? It's not as if I can drive you about. I wouldn't anyway, even if I could.' Occasionally drifting into a semi-slumber she forgot he wasn't there until she turned round to cuddle him only to find his side of the bed cold. Funny how you could even come to miss your husband's snoring.

Rita's alarm was set for 4 a.m., but she didn't need it. She hadn't slept a wink. She got up just before four, took a quick bath and changed into jeans and her overall. She sat at her dressing table, looking out of the window waiting for the taxi and chewing a nail. The sky grew slowly paler and in the east a pink tinge on the horizon pointed to a bright dawn. Rita often thought spring was the saddest season of all – she would get melancholic, anticipating the end of the warm days before they'd even started. She was definitely a 'glass is half empty' woman, just as Douggie was a 'glass is half full' kind of man. She grew to miss the boring nights when they sat in front of the television sniping at each other and bickering about money and the children. She missed watching him wolf his dinner down and then stretching with satiated pleasure, or bellowing at Ronnie to pick up his stuff: 'Do as your mother tells you, she's not here to run around after you, you little prick.'

Douggie wasn't home. Lately he'd been making it back anywhere between 1.30 and 3 a.m., which was bad enough, but twenty-past four was worrying. Pride prevented her from calling the club – she had always refused to be the kind of woman who rang around in a small-hours panic looking for her husband; it just made a laughing stock of the pair of them. Her heart gave a little lift when she saw headlights coming up Foxley Lane and indicating to turn in on her side of the street. But in the growing light she saw it was not his Mercedes but a dark Granada, and when the minicab hooted outside the house she trailed heavily down the stairs, closed the door quietly behind her and slumped in the back. Thankfully it wasn't her usual driver Don, so she didn't have to make much conversation.

Within twenty minutes she was getting out of the cab at New Covent Garden, already full with traders and shop-keepers. She trailed desultorily round the market, picking up boxes of flowers, unable to concentrate. Being pissed off with Douggie was far preferable to being worried about him and she tried to think of the reasons that might make him late. Not having been to the club, she couldn't even picture what he might be doing. She longed for the days when he would get home an hour late from the car lot. She knew then that he either had a late customer, was taking a delivery of parts or just sodding about in the pub with Gully.

Rita loaded a box of dark red roses on to her trolley. They reminded her of her wedding bouquet.

She would have liked to blame their current *froideur* on the club, but it must be something else. Why get the club in the first place if he was happy with her? Maybe he'd been looking for an excuse to get out of the house. Perhaps it was her fault after all; maybe she had been so busy with the shop and the house she had forgotten about him. She still made his dinners, cleaned his house, cared for his children and even made love to him a couple of times a month, but she didn't know that she could honestly claim she was still in love with him, if indeed she ever had been. Maybe he'd finally tumbled and decided to find his comfort elsewhere. She cast her mind back to their early days and tried to recall what she used to feel. Was there a difference between love and *in* love? She fingered some long Bird of Paradise stems that she'd seen in the hearth at Doreen and Frank's. She certainly loved Douggie and had enjoyed their happy years together, but it wasn't what she'd felt for the other one, even knowing he couldn't love her the way Douggie did or give her the family life she treasured so much.

She decided against the Birds of Paradise and loaded up a couple of boxes of peonies instead. She would never have been able to trust him the way she trusted Douggie. She'd told herself for twenty-odd years she'd done the right thing and had had no reason to doubt that. Until now. Even in the early days of their marriage when Frank was still around she'd had no cause to regret marrying Doug – compared to Douggie Fisher he was a cruel bully, a man without loyalty. But why feel this way again now? It shouldn't affect her, him being back in their lives, but it did. She was scared to see him, to be near him, because she couldn't stand the truth of her own feelings. She loved him in a way she'd never loved her husband. Absent-mindedly she loaded up with freesias, forgetting she still had several dozen back at the shop.

And now what? She guessed she'd reached the age where you start to look back instead of forwards, the only surprises on the horizon being grandchildren. Rita used to love to dream of the future. Wanting a husband, getting one.

Wanting a family, getting one. Wanting a better house, a nicer area and getting those things too. It had all gone by so quick. No more looking forwards. The children were good: not brilliant, but not sick or in trouble. Now life was no longer what would be but what could have been. Had she, after all, robbed herself of the chance of sharing her life with the one she truly loved?

She spent the journey from Covent Garden to the shop in South Croydon daydreaming and by the time the minicab stopped, her thoughts had come full circle. She told herself that she was young then, a different woman who didn't know what love was. Even if she had been 'in love' with him, he was still a bastard. She resolved to stay out of his way until these feelings passed. It was because Doug left her alone with too much time to think. She'd just get busy again, plan a holiday, bring some brochures home for Doug to look at. This brought her back to her original worry. Where the hell was he?

She found him sooner than she'd expected. As she unloaded the boxes of flowers from the back of the cab, something caught her eye. There, slumped in the doorway of RITA'S, was the sleeping figure of her husband. The corners of her mouth turned up in wry appreciation and she had to stifle a laugh and remind herself to be angry with him. She kicked the prone figure into consciousness. 'Where have you been? I've been worried sick.' Then remembering the driver, she turned back and handed him a £10 note: 'Cheers, tell Don I'll see him on Monday.'

Douggie came round and squinted up at his wife, who stood in front of a bright sun. 'Come on, get up you useless bloody lump. Look at the state of you. Carry these boxes in.'

Rita stepped over him and unlocked the door, then quickly switched off the alarm. Douggie stuttered, 'Rita love, I'm sorry, it's just that they towed the car' – he stumbled into the shop – 'and all my house keys are in it and I didn't want to wake you up.'

Rita dumped her handbag behind the counter, took the receipts from the market out of her pocket and impaled them roughly on the spike where she kept the bills, making Douggie wince. As she slipped her arms out of her coat she stared at him expectantly. 'And how long have you been dossing in the doorway like a tramp? You couldn't have been there all night. I know you, you can't sleep if it's cold.'

'Yeah all right, turn it down, I'll tell you later.' Douggie stumbled to his feet. 'Put the kettle on, love, I'm parched.'

Rita clicked out to the back of the shop, flicked the kettle on and applied lipstick, then marched back to find Doug slumped in the chair she kept in the shop for the old girls who came in to order funeral wreaths. 'Look at the bloody state of you.' Rita allowed herself a laugh at the spectacle of her husband. Tie hanging out of his jacket pocket, collar askew, flies half undone and what looked like barbecue sauce down the front of his shirt. One of his cufflinks was missing and both shoe-laces were undone. Rita kissed him lightly. 'You bloody stink of booze – have a good one, did you?'

'Look, I'm sorry, love, we were playing cards.' He put his hands up to stall the next inevitable question: 'And I didn't want to ring you and wake you up, because I knew you had to get up to go to the market, all right?

'Anyway, when I came out of the club at 5.30, the bloody car had gone. Either it's been nicked or the Old Bill have decided to revoke our privileges, which is a fucking cheek when you consider.'

'Just as well, by the looks of it. You'd have killed yourself. You can't keep driving home pissed, Douggie, they'll get you one of these days. What do you mean "when you consider"? Why do the police have to do you any favours?'

'No, I just meant, I thought we had an arrangement, you know, Frank and the cones. Where's that tea?'

'Mmm.' Rita didn't look convinced but was just pleased

to see him in one piece. 'Go over to the caff and get a couple of bacon sandwiches – plenty of brown sauce on mine, please.' Douggie checked his pockets and could find only a few coppers in change, so he took a fiver out of Rita's purse. 'Back in a minute,' he called out, but she had seen him through the little one-way glass at the back of the shop. He must have lost all of his money at cards. 'I'll kill him,' she said to herself.

She let the teabags brew in the mugs and stacked the boxes of flowers in the fridges. She turned on her blow heater behind the counter, then the radio and the lights, and after ignoring the phone for a few rings, picked up the receiver.

'Mavis, hello love, what's up?' It was Rita's younger sister, who'd been helping her in the shop since Marilyn left. It had seemed like a good idea at the time, but Rita was beginning to have second thoughts. Like most sibling relationships, theirs had settled into cordial affection after the tempests of their youth but in middle age their differences were no less marked. Rita had been the good one, getting a place at gram-mar school, even managing a few O levels. She'd always been the one with the steady marriage, the good husband and the kids hardly ever in trouble. Mavis had been the wild one. Pregnant at fifteen, now with an adopted child somewhere in Australia and three others at home with her ignorant husband Jim in Camberwell. They were a right bunch of rascals – only her daughter Cindy seemed to have had anything going for her at all with her job as a fitness instructor at the local leisure centre until she got thrown out for dealing.

'We've had a row, Rita, I'm not coming in, not with this black eye. Mind you, he don't look too clever either; I gave as good as I got. Fucking bastard.'

'Well can't you just make up bouquets for me out the back? I'll serve the customers. I really need you today Mave, I've just picked up a load of new stock.'

Mavis was adamant that she couldn't make it in, but could

really do with seeing Rita for a chat later. Rita guessed correctly that she was hung over as well. It was always the drink that set those two off.

'Yeah, go on then, come over tonight, I'll send Doug down the pub and I shouldn't think the kids will be at home. All right then love, but leave it till about eight, yeah? I won't be back from the shop till half-six, it'll give me a chance to jump in the bath and get a bit of tea ready.' Rita held the receiver away from her ear as Mavis's voice rose to a noisy, tearful pitch: 'Just calm down, all right, and stay out of his way. I'll see you tonight.'

Douggie came back with the bacon sandwiches as Rita was putting the receiver down with a sigh. 'Mavis,' She explained. 'Jim thumped her again and she's not coming in.'

'He's a fucking animal, she should have packed it in years ago.' Douggie shoved a big dripping sandwich in his mouth.

'Yeah, well, no such thing as a perfect marriage, eh Doug? So, what happened?' She'd heard it all before, but having him before her in one piece was a relief.

'Well you're not going in on Saturday night, we're going out for dinner.'

'Who with?' Douggie licked the grease from his fingers and slurped his tea.

'I don't know yet, but I'm not spending another Saturday night on my own watching bleeding Russ Abbott, so you can tell Frank, Mark, whoever, that you won't be there.'

'I can't let Frank down.'

'How many times has Frank been at that club since you started?' Douggie mumbled something about him being busy so Rita interrupted, 'See? He doesn't give a monkey's, I bet he goes out with his wife at the weekend. You can too. Steve can cover your shift.' This wasn't the time to argue the toss with her. He was relieved that he'd got off so lightly. 'For goodness' sake Douggie, go home, have a bath and go to bed.'

'Got a quid for the bus, love?'

Mavis couldn't wait. Five minutes after Rita walked through the front door, she recognised her sister's insistent ring on the doorbell. 'Get the door, Ronnie, it's your Auntie Mave, tell her I'm in the bath.'

Rita legged it up the stairs. She needed ten minutes on her own to collect her thoughts before she set about putting Mavis's world to rights. She loved her sister, but often wondered if she wasn't just as much to blame for the state of her home life as the useless twit she was married to. Mavis had always been a handful. Rita recalled the time when Mavis had nicked her best woollen blankets, engagement presents that she kept in her bottom drawer, and took them on the Ban the Bomb march to Aldermaston. Came back all filthy and covered in crap. Rita had been devastated and Mavis's only response had been to accuse her big sister of being uptight: that still stuck in her craw.

While Rita lay back in the bath and closed her eyes, Ronnie tried to keep his Auntie Mave entertained downstairs.

'Get us a drink, Ronnie. Your mum got any nice brandy, that Courvoisier? Stick a bit of lemonade in with it and plenty of ice. Ta, love.' Mavis wandered round the kitchen looking for Rita's bag and when she found it, took out her cigarettes. She had her own cigarettes, but figured that as Rita had more money, she should smoke hers instead. Mavis never smoked her own fags if she could help it and the way she just helped herself to other people's without even asking infuriated Rita. All day at the shop, Mavis would smoke Rita's Rothmans while her own packet of Silk Cut sat untouched on the desk out the back. Rita didn't like Silk Cut, or she'd have given her sister a taste of her own medicine. It was bloody annoying if you thought you had enough for the day to have to go next door to get more at lunchtime.

It was the attitude that she could just take from other people that really got to Rita.

Mavis and Jim were seasoned ponces who believed that it was the government's responsibility to keep them. The whole family signed on, had the rent paid by the social and finagled every single extra they could. They were expert fraudsters and were resentful of people who had more. The fact that the objects of their derision might have worked hard for their beloved homes and cars cut little ice with Mavis and Jim Ramsay. Douggie reckoned it was because Jim was half Scottish that he was so tight, but Rita knew they were just a couple of shiftless gits. At least her sister had a roughish charm and a saucy laugh, but Jim could really make her blood boil when he sat there drinking their booze and telling them how lucky they were.

Rita had still not quite forgiven Mavis for her behaviour at their mother's funeral. After leaving South London Crematorium they had retired to Lillian's little flat on the Waddon Estate for tea, sandwiches and a drop of the hard stuff. Mavis knocked back far too much brandy, got lairy and started inviting all the old bids to go through Lillian's drawers and take what they wanted. Rita considered this tacky beyond belief and became anguished at the sight of her mother's sisters and friends raiding her tallboy and trying on her old cardigans and dresses. Rita knew that Mavis was still smarting because Lillian had given Rita the diamond and sapphire ring, and her plain gold wedding band to her younger daughter. Mavis had thrown the ring across the room saying, 'I don't want this piece of shit, give it to Marilyn' and Rita had said, 'Well if that's your attitude, I will.' She bloody did, too.

Ronnie handed his Auntie Mave her drink, a look of vague disgust hovering on his features. She took a sip, winced and handed the glass back to him: 'Bit weak, love, stick some more brandy in there.' Ronnie did as he was told and silently prayed for his mother to hurry up. He couldn't stand her side of the family as a rule, whereas his dad's brothers were a really friendly bunch, had loads of parties, and he got on really well with his cousins on that side.

He poured a great slug of brandy into the glass, filling it to the brim, hoping the strength would choke her. She tested it again and proclaimed it to be 'just right'. With her sister's fags and booze in hand, she settled into Douggie's big chair in the front room, its occupant having vacated the house at opening time, not planning to return until closing. The standard question followed: 'So then Ron, how are you getting on at school? Your mum says you're doing eight O levels, you're very lucky.'

'What's lucky about it?'

'Well, going to that posh school. You've had a lot more chances than my lot.'

'I don't think it matters so much what school you go to, Auntie Mave. The trick is to turn up occasionally.'

She shot him a hateful look. Too bloody cocky for his own good, that one. 'What's your mother up to?' she asked.

'She'll be down in a minute.' Ronnie scratched his head. 'Auntie Mave, do you mind, I've got a lot of homework . . .'

'No, go on then, I'm used to being left on my own. I'm sure you've got better things to do than sit with the poor relations.'

Ronnie hissed, 'Stupid old cow' and turned to leave the room, bumping into his mother as he did so.

'I heard that,' Rita said. 'All right, Mave?' Her tone was bright, as if to lift the inevitable downward drift of mood which would descend after half an hour in her sister's company. Looking at her glass she said, 'Seeing as you're having one, I might as well join you.'

'I don't know how you get through the evening without one.'

'I'm usually too knackered to even think about a drink.'

'All right for people with jobs, I suppose.'

Rita bit her tongue; it was going to be a long evening and she didn't want to start off on the back foot.

'Look,' Mavis commanded, standing under the light, the better for Rita to see the swelling under her left eye. 'It hasn't all come out yet, but it'll be black and blue by tomorrow.'

'What started it off this time, then?' Rita settled on the sofa across from her sister and sucked the frothy head from the bottled Guinness she'd poured into her glass. She braced herself.

'Came back totally pissed from the White Hart as usual. Lairy as fuck, wanting to know where his tea was. So I told him, I says, "In the fuckin' bin, you bastard. If you want your tea you get back here at teatime." Well that was it, weren't it, he did his nut. Then the bloody dog comes down and starts yapping, so he kicks my Jess and then I really lost it. You know how that dog loves me and protects me, I'd die for that dog.'

Rita allowed herself a little smile. Indeed she did know how that dog loved Mavis. Wasn't a bad animal really, it was just that Jim, nasty bastard that he was, had trained it to growl at black people. Living in Camberwell, this became something of a full-time job for the dog. Among their other charms, Mavis and Jim were dreadful bigots – 'I mean you just have to walk into a Paki shop and take a whiff to know what filthy bastards they are, not that I ever would, mind. I'd rather walk the extra half a mile to Sainsbury's to do my shopping. Bunch of fucking rip-off merchants, they're making a bloody fortune out of us, then they bring all their bloody relations over – straight off the plane, down the social and into a house. Makes me sick.'

Rita sighed deeply. If her sister would just shut up for a minute she might even like to have a good moan herself, but something about Mave's hostility and self-absorption put her off.

'Look Mave, I know I've said this a thousand times, but why don't you just leave? You've said yourself, you don't love him any more, the kids are almost grown up. The council would have to rehouse you if you told them he was violent.'

'Oh no I wouldn't do that, Reet. I mean, he's my husband after all, I'm not telling some fucking stranger down the social about my marriage.' Doesn't stop you taking their money though, does it, Rita wanted to add, but reminded herself that she was blood after all. For better or worse, she just had to stand by her. Mavis had no more intention of leaving Jim now than she had in the last twenty-three years when the beatings had started on their honeymoon on the Isle of Wight.

'No, he's all right, Reet, he's a good man, my Jim, he just gets a temper on him when he drinks that Southern Comfort. I've told him, I said, "You're all right when you drink ordinary Scotch" – I mean, he can drink buckets of that and he's fine, but the minute he goes near that bleeding Southern Comfort . . . God knows what they put in it – honestly, I feel like writing to them sometimes.'

Thus the evening passed. Douggie arrived home at about 10.30 hoping to have missed his sister-in-law, but no such luck. He was pleased that he'd had the foresight to drink seven pints, because Mavis's first words to him were not friendly: 'Blimey, look who's here, old Rockefeller himself. Been down at the bank counting your millions then, Doug?'

'Don't talk shit, Mavis, you know I haven't got that kind of money. Your sister spent it all.' Douggie laughed uproariously at his own joke and from where she was listening in the kitchen, Rita was relieved to hear that he was pissed and feeling mellow. Water off a duck's back when he was in this kind of a mood. Even Rita couldn't get to him when he felt like that.

Douggie staggered over to Mavis and kissed her on the cheek. 'Well fuck me, Mave, you smell of my best brandy, now there's a turn-up.' Not pausing long enough to hear her tart reply, Douggie wove his way across the room a little unsteadily. Slipping his jacket off in the hall he called out, 'Rita, where are you?'

'I'm in here, and don't shout, Ronnie's in bed.' Douggie found her in the kitchen buttering some toast for her sister to help soak up the Courvoisier and making a cup of tea for herself.

'When's she going home?' Douggie asked.

'Sshh. Keep your voice down, she can hear you.'

'Get rid of her, I want to talk to you. Can't talk to you with old misery-guts next door.' Douggie swayed, leaning against the sink.

'Talk about what?'

'Me and you, Reet. I know we've had our rows before, but this is something else. I dunno, you just seem really cold, I feel like I'm losing you.' He slumped at the kitchen table and began to eat Mavis's toast. Rita was shocked. Douggie never talked about things unless she forced him to.

'Do you love me, Rita?' He looked her in the eye when he said it. She replied indignantly: 'Of course I love you, don't be so bloody stupid, we've been married for donkey's years. Honestly Douggie, you do talk rubbish when you're pissed.' She lit a cigarette and slurped her hot tea noisily.

'Look at me, Rita' – he grabbed her hand. 'I know all that bollocks about being married for twenty-six years, but do you love me?'

'I said yes, didn't I?' She dismissed him impatiently.

'No, don't get like that. Answer the question. Do you really love me, Rita? Not "Do you think I'm a good husband and father who's taken care of you?", I know all that. I want to know if you really love me. Love me like I love you.'

Rita was so taken aback she couldn't speak. Had he turned

into a mind-reader all of a sudden? She turned away from him so he couldn't see the tears welling up in her eyes.

'Come on, answer me,' he said.

'I don't know,' she said softly.

'That means no, doesn't it?'

'No, it means I don't know.'

'Did you ever love me, Rita?' His voice was calm but defeated.

'Of course I did, Douggie.'

'What, but you don't any more?'

'Oh, shit Douggie, I don't know.'

'Have you ever been in love with anybody else?'

They sat in silence for several moments. Rita was still trying to pluck up the courage to answer, when her sister wobbled into view. 'Were you supposed to be making me a bit of toast, Rita?' Mavis demanded angrily.

'Oh for crying out loud, make your own bloody toast, I'm talking.'

'Was it anybody I know?' Douggie asked.

'No,' she lied.

Can It Be That It Was All So Simple Then?

1972 – Part One

On 4 November 1971 Rita sat in the public gallery of Kennington Court and exhaled with relief when Douggie was sentenced to six years' imprisonment for his part in the Mitcham warehouse robbery. With good behaviour and parole he would be out in four.

It could have been worse. When the arrests were first made, the police had been baying for blood. The robbery had featured heavily in the papers with much being made of the gunshot wound to the shoulder sustained by one of the nightwatchmen and the death of his Alsatian dog. The London firms were getting away with too much; security had yet to catch up with the use of firearms in robberies. But Douggie, unusually, had been smart. By giving the appearance of total co-operation with the police – once they caught him – and at the same time saving Frank Skinner's neck by denying his involvement, he bought himself not just the favour of the forces of law and a correspondingly brief sentence, but more importantly the assured protection of his family while he was in prison. Tempting though it might have been to grass on Frank, there was no one else who could afford to provide for Rita and the kids and no matter how loudly Douggie squealed he was never going to walk free. The police knew that Skinner had masterminded the job but weren't too bothered as long as they secured convictions for the other three men involved. As much as it could be said of such a state of affairs, everybody was happy.

Douggie winked at his pregnant wife as he was led out of

the dock to be taken to Parkhurst Prison on the Isle of Wight. She smiled at him softly with tears in her eyes, knowing that this was the turning point in their lives. They'd talked about it for a couple of years; the children were beginning to understand about life and Douggie and Rita agreed that they didn't want them growing up with a jobbing-crim for a dad. At ten, Steve was shrewd enough to keep quiet about his father's activities but Marilyn was five and had a mouth on her. That summer Gully had caught her swanking around outside Stockwell tube station in her purple suede hotpants with the black apple and long laces, saying to anyone that would listen: 'Do you like my hotpants? My dad nicked 'em.'

Ronnie was due late November and his mum and dad were adamant that their kids' generation would be the first on either side of the family with honest working parents. Douggie knew before the Mitcham job that his criminal career was grinding to a close and they'd both almost welcomed his arrest. Rita knew better than to go on at Douggie about getting a job before he was ready to stop; besides, in his quieter moments he admitted that his nerves couldn't really take it any more. He wasn't cut out of the same mould as Frank Skinner; having to use guns made him jittery, besides which he had no interest in money for its own sake, just the fun it could bring.

Douggie's mum, Olive, took Rita's arm and helped her out of the courthouse and down the steps into a biting wind that blasted along Kennington Lane. The baby was due soon and Rita was as big as a house. 'It'll be a ten-pounder, Reet, the last baby is always the biggest. Look at me with Douggie. I was in labour all weekend trying to get that bugger out.'

'Thanks, Olive, I needed something to cheer me up.'

The two women waddled slowly to the bus stop, Rita pulling her short coat close to her. She couldn't do it up properly and held her handbag in front of her bump to shield it from the wind. Her legs froze in her minidress and she wished they'd had enough money to buy some decent maternity clothes.

A bus pulled up after about five minutes and the two women climbed to the top deck and settled in the small two-seater at the back. 'The love seat,' Rita called it. She and Douggie had done a lot of their courting in the back seat of the 159, shielded from the eyes of the other passengers. Olive lit them both a cigarette and Rita sucked hard, staring thoughtfully out of the window. Olive took her hand and squeezed. 'Never mind, eh love? He'll be back before you know it and back for good an' all. He's a good boy Douggie, he knows when to give it up. Not like his father, the bastard. My George didn't even have the decency to get out in time to die. I've never forgiven him for having his stroke in prison.'

'Mmm. I could murder a Guinness, Olive. Can we stop at the Angel before going back to the flat? I can't face seeing Mum and the kids just yet. Steve's really upset about his dad.' Rita twisted her lacy hanky around her fingers tightly in an effort to cauterise the pain.

'Course we can, love. Not too many though, madam, I'm not having you getting pissed and falling over with my grandson inside you.'

'We don't know that it's a boy yet, Olive.' Rita was irritated by the way Douggie's mum had correctly predicted the sex of each of her children. It took all the fun out of it.

'Of course it's a boy. Look at you, you're the size of a bleedin' bus and you're carrying all round like you did with Steve. You carried Marilyn up front, remember?'

'Yeah, but me and Douggie like surprises, we don't want to know.'

'Well, what difference does it make? He's not going to be there. You're on your own now Rita, you better get used to it.'

'Do you have to be such a fucking doom merchant, Olive?'

'Stop feeling sorry for yourself. Plenty of women have to manage on their own. Look at the war, we didn't have a choice.' Rita swallowed the impulse to point out that George had been a draft-dodger.

She turned her head to stare at the bitter profile of her mother-in-law. Her thin lips drew tight around her untipped fag and her brow was set in a line of permanent consternation. The thinning hair was tinted purple, her pink scalp showing through, and the lined jowls quivered with sour animation. She wouldn't have minded Olive's coat, though. It was gorgeous. Pure grey wool, belted with a fur collar. George's last gift to his wife. Rita wished that Olive would lend it to her until she had the baby. It would fit her nicely. Olive's stomach was almost as big as Rita's and although the doctors repeatedly told Olive Fisher that she was suffering from wind, when they opened her up a few years hence, they would find a tumour the size of a football. Terrible, really.

Olive blew out a jet of smoke and sighed. 'Besides, they only get under your feet, men.'

The bus stopped on Brixton Road and the conductor helped Rita down the steps, holding her hand securely. Olive looked on disapprovingly and before the bus pulled out of earshot spat, 'Fucking nig-nog, who does he think he is, touching you like that?' Rita felt a rush of hot blood to her head and screamed, 'For crying out loud, Olive, just shut up, he was only helping me. You make me sick the way you go on about them, they're just people!'

Olive Fisher had won a few fights in her time, but had learned not to rile her daughter-in-law. Rita's anger could switch from ice to fire and back again in such quick succession that it made it hard for any opponent to stand their ground. Rita Fisher could not be beat in an argument; she was completely unafraid.

'All right, darlin', calm down. It was just a joke.'

'No it wasn't. And I'm fed up with the way you keep pointing them out to Marilyn as coons when you take her shopping – it's disgusting.' Rita marched her great weight purposefully forwards. Olive kept pace with difficulty.

'I'm sorry, Rita, but you can't stand there and tell me that they don't come over here and take all our council houses and jobs.'

'I haven't seen you looking for a job. Still claiming George's social?' Rita went for the Achilles – Olive Fisher had a few fiddles going on the social security, perhaps the most admirable being the continuing claim of benefit for a deceased husband of fifteen years. Rita had her bang to rights and she knew it.

'Don't get out of your pram, you'll go into labour. Now come on, calm down, we'll get you that stout.' In angry silence they walked the last hundred yards to the pub.

They entered the lunchtime fug of the Angel and Rita smiled wanly at Bill the landlord as she settled herself in a chair. Noting her arrival, the pub grew quiet and pint mugs were gently lowered on to bar towels in the expectant hush. 'How did you get on love?' Bill asked.

'Six,' said Rita quietly. A sympathetic murmur rumbled and a couple of the regulars came over to pat her hand and reassure her that time passed quickly. Rita wasn't in the mood for a post-mortem but Olive gladly took up the mantle, blaming everybody except her guilty son and saying at every opportunity, 'Well of course if he'd been foreign he'd have got away with it. It's all wrong, if you ask me.'

Rita was too tired to manage anything but a look of disgust.

Bill's wife Dolly brought a bottle of Guinness over to Rita and sat for a while talking quietly about the baby clothes she'd managed to cobble together for the imminent arrival.

'Thanks, Dolly. You're a real mate. I couldn't manage

without you now I'm on my own,' said Rita.

'You're not on your own, I'm going to take ⟨
came a voice from behind. Rita turned and fo
clean lines of a Tonik suit to the face at the top. ⟨
heaved herself out of her chair to square up to him b
spoke: 'You've got a nerve, Frank Skinner.'

Rita's first words to her infant son were, 'What time do you call this then, eh?'

Ronald Douglas Fisher arrived one month late on 22 December, purple as a bishop's cloak, weighing in at a whopping 10 pounds 3 ounces at St James' Hospital, Balham. Attending the birth were Ronnie's grandmothers Olive and Lillian, women who, even under normal circumstances, found the exchange of pleasantries hard going. The occasion of the fatherless birth simply served to make it worse. They bickered for the entire seven hours Rita was in labour about the best way Master Ronald Douglas should be brought into the world.

'Push, Rita. If you don't get it out, the poor little sod will choke to death,' advised Olive.

'Just keep breathing love, don't push yet. You haven't opened up enough, anyone can see that,' countered Lillian in a tone which suggested that the dilation of cervixes was something she studied on a daily basis. A midwife hovered superfluously in the background, occasionally inserting a finger into Rita to check the position of the baby's head. The grandmothers would tut when the midwife blocked their view by having the gall to try to examine Rita and offer words of encouragement. Rita would look at her imploringly but if she wanted them out of her sight she would have to get up and walk. The two battleaxes had their sleeves rolled up for the duration.

Rita had wanted only her mum, Lillian, to assist in the labour but Olive had been adamant that in the absence of ggie, a representative of the Fishers should be on hand to witness the event.

'It's really sweet of you to offer, Olive, but don't worry, it's not as if Douggie would have been here anyway.'

'He was there when Marilyn was born,' harrumphed Olive.

'Only because she came before I had the chance to get to the hospital and Douggie always stopped in on a Wednesday night to watch *The Fugitive*.'

Christmas Eve, two days after his birth, Rita took her baby son home in a taxi to meet his brother and sister for the first time. Marilyn came rushing out on to the landing when she heard her mother coming up the stairs and almost flung herself into Ronnie's carrycot with excitement. Rita noticed with annoyance that her mother had pulled Marilyn's hair into a tight bun on top of her head – she preferred her daughter's blonde wavy hair to fall around her plump face, slimming it down a bit.

'Blimey Marilyn, let me get in the door, love.'

Rita bouldered into the front room to be confronted by red roses resting on every available surface – stuffed in glasses, old jam jars and her one decent vase. There must have been about four dozen of them.

'I've spent all bloody morning trying to sort this lot out, it's no good having this many flowers in the house using up all the air with a baby,' said Rita's mother. 'There's a card on the table, I don't know who it's from. Can't be short of a bob or two, whoever it is.'

Rita knew straight away and neither opened the card nor told her mum who the flowers were from.

She rested the carrycot on the counter dividing the front room from the kitchen and took off her coat. Her ten-year-old son slouched silently on the settee. Rita walked over to him and ruffled his hair. 'What's the matter, love, you all miserable? Come and have a look at your little brother.'

Steven stared straight ahead, not catching his mother's eye. He kicked his feet against the base of the settee and asked, 'Can we call him Peter Osgood Fisher?'

'No, love, his name is Ronnie.'

'What about Gordon Fisher, after Gordon Banks?'

Rita laughed and hugged her son to her still full stomach. Steve started to cry, wiping the snot on the sleeve of his Chelsea football shirt. Rita pulled her hanky out of her sleeve and dabbed his eyes, shushing him quietly. Poor little sod, missed his dad so much. To a ten-year-old, four years was almost for ever. Marilyn and Lillian, oblivious, were fighting over the baby. 'Let me hold him, Nan, let me hold him,' said Marilyn, grasping at the swaddled infant.

'Make sure you don't bloody drop him. Sit still on that chair and keep quiet while I make your mother a cup of tea.'

'Marilyn, bring Ronnie over here and let Steve hold him.'

'Oh Mum, I've only just got him.' She gripped the child tighter to her.

'Do as you're told and get these flowers out of the way. Go on, put them in your bedroom.'

'What, all of 'em?'

'Yes, you can keep all of them, Marilyn, but make sure you open your window a little bit.'

Suitably distracted from her new brother by the idea of four dozen red roses in her bedroom, Marilyn handed over the baby without hesitation. Steve looked curious and poked the baby's stomach, sniffing loudly.

'Careful love, he's only tiny.' Rita rubbed Steve's arm.

'He's a funny colour.'

'That's because he was late; all overdue babies are that colour. He'll soon be normal.'

'He won't be able to play football for ages yet, though. Why didn't you have him before Marilyn? She's an idiot.'

'You don't get any say in the matter. You have to take what the stork gives you.' Rita smiled to see her tiny son looking up at his brother.

Lillian placed a cup of tea before her daughter. The sun shone warmly into the front room and the gas fire was going full blast. But Rita felt a chill, as if somebody was looking at her. In a manner of speaking, they were.

Their two-bedroom flat above the greengrocer's was far from spacious. They'd been stretched for room with two children, and a third was pushing it. Douggie had made a partition in their bedroom to create a separate room for Steve. It was narrow and dark with a high ceiling, but they'd let him poster the walls freely with pictures of his football idols and given him a big record player, so he was happy.

Marilyn had a nice little room of her own at the back of the flat with a window that opened on to a flat bit of roof where you could sit when it was warm. In the summer holidays, Marilyn and Steve would perch out there and call down to their mates playing in the alley below to come up. Rita had tried to keep the numbers down, but she couldn't be with them every minute. She made regular trips to the bedroom window to check on them. New children would arrive after each visit when Rita wasn't looking and although the flat of the roof measured no more than eight feet by four, six or seven children could muck about comfortably. Rita did worry about the twelve-foot drop to the pavement, and once they began sodding about with the old washing-up bottles having water fights, she'd put her foot down and make them go and play in the alley.

Christmas and the coming of 1972 passed quietly in the Fisher flat. While Lillian minded Ronnie, Rita took Marilyn and Steve to Brixton market late on Christmas Eve to pick out a small tree and see if there were any butchers still open so she could get a bird for the next day. Dolly from the Angel had promised to sort out the trimmings for her and was hanging on to the toys that Rita had bought with her Christmas Club money before she went into hospital.

Rita called into the pub with the two kids at around seven o'clock. It was the lull before the storm; the lunchtime drinkers had been evicted sharp at 4 p.m. after a short lock-in so Dolly and Bill could put their feet up before the evening shift. Everyone would be at home now, having their tea and polishing up for the night's celebrations.

Rita ordered a bottle of Guinness for herself and two shandies for the kids. Once they'd been given their drinks and some crisps, Dolly ordered them out the back to help Bill cut the sausage rolls and put the nibbles out for later. The bar was dripping with tinsel in red, gold, silver and green, the ceiling heavy with hanging ornaments and paper chains. Bill had spent the afternoon blowing up five bags of balloons that he knew would fall victim to stray fags before midnight struck. Dolly looked lovely. She'd had her red hair set in curlers, donned her false eyelashes and carefully applied green shadow with gold glitter along the eyeline. Gold bell-bottoms were topped with a red spangly halter-neck top. She was very modern for a woman in her forties.

'Bit knackered then, Reet?' Dolly was polishing glasses.

'Not too bad, Doll. He's a really good baby, he's hardly cried at all. Got any fags, Dolly? I left mine indoors.'

Dolly reached behind the till and pulled out forty Number Six and an envelope. She held them up until she'd finished speaking.

'Now listen, before you start saying it's too much and you can't take it, remember that we wouldn't do it if we didn't want to. Anyway, Bill had a little win on the horses last week so we're flush.' Dolly handed the envelope and cigarettes over the bar. 'And don't open it until you get home. You coming in later?'

'No, I'd better stay in with Mum and the kids. I've got to wrap their presents up.' Rita fingered the envelope. 'Look,

Dolly, it's really generous of you and Bill, but—'

'I told you to shut up about it, Rita. I don't want to hear another word. I'll nip over later with the presents when they're in bed and we can have a little drink with your mum.'

'You can't leave the pub, Doll. It's your busiest night.'

'I can do what I bloody well like, it's my pub. Anyway, we've got extra staff, they won't miss me for half an hour. Hold on, I've got some decorations out the back for your tree.' Dolly clomped in her platforms into the hallway behind the bar and shouted something to her husband. She stomped back with an order:

'Go on, go home and have a bath in peace and quiet. I'll get Bill to bring the kids back in about an hour.' Dolly wiped an ashtray and carefully lined it up parallel to a bar towel. She could see the uncertainty on Rita's face. 'Go on, they'll be all right, I'll give them a bit of money for the fruit machines. They can muck about in here or go next door and watch the telly.'

'Are you sure, Dolly?'

'Oh piss off, Rita, you're getting boring.'

Rita used the hour alone to feed Ronnie and steal about fifteen red roses from Marilyn's bedroom to tie to the tree. She cut the stalks short and secured them with darning wool. Dolly had put some fairy lights in the bag, which Rita trailed around the tree and plugged in.

'Ah, it looks lovely, Rita.' Lillian was at the sink peeling enough potatoes for an army in readiness for lunch the following day.

'Yeah, it's not too bad is it, Mum?' Rita leaned back, resting her weight on her heels, her hands folded in her lap as she admired her handiwork. On the floor her baby son slept soundly in his carrycot. 'He's such an angel, Mum, look at him, good as gold.'

'Yeah, dead spit of his dad an' all,' smiled his grandmother.

Rita looked at her mother's tired face bent over the sink, the mountain of potatoes piling up in her big saucepan. 'Mum, come and sit down. Get a bottle of Guinness out of the cupboard and put your feet up.'

'All right love, I'll just finish these spuds. Actually, I've got a bottle of port that I won in the raffle at the bingo last week. Do you fancy a port and lemonade?'

Rita smacked her lips. 'Oh, I'd love one, Mum. Come on, come and sit down and have a fag.'

Lillian and Rita settled on the threadbare sofa with their drinks, the carrycot between them and an ashtray resting on its cover. On the television, Benny Hill was doing a Christmas special and Rita laughed despite herself. She didn't find him that funny, but the memory of Douggie watching him with tears rolling down his puce face, his body doubled over with laughter, forced a smile. Ronnie didn't murmur – even when Steve and Marilyn came back from the pub shouting and screaming, all excited. Bill had obviously given them more than a couple of shandies and filled their pockets with change. Both were wearing paper hats and brandishing toys from crackers. Marilyn kicked up a bit of a fuss when she saw that some of her roses had been commandeered for the decoration of the tree, but had to admit that they looked pretty. Rita had saved the tinsel and the balls for the two children to drape where they wanted on the tree.

She watched as they fought over the thickest piece of tinsel and the big shiny gold bells and thought that if Douggie was here he'd work the kids up into a frenzy, chase them round the flat and get them all excited so they wouldn't sleep. He'd probably be as pissed as a parrot too, love him. She felt a stab of longing so sharp she had to put her hand to her stomach.

By midnight the children were in bed, though unlikely to be asleep. Lillian was snoring in a chair and only Rita and Ronnie were awake for the first moments of Christmas Day.

She pulled her tiny son to her breast and whispered, 'Happy Christmas my little love. Go on, have a drink.'

She knew it was only a matter of time before he showed his face. Like lightning heralding thunder, gifts for the baby began arriving shortly after the New Year. Rita's mum raised her eyebrows when the cot arrived from John Lewis but said nothing; Lillian had seen enough comings and goings of luxury goods in her daughter's married life to know to keep her head down. ·

Once the fuss of Douggie's departure, Ronnie's arrival and Christmas had died down, the grandmothers began to fade from Rita's routine. Lillian had turned up at the flat on New Year's Day, distraught at the news that Maurice Chevalier had died, but apart from that and Dolly's daily visits, life continued as before. The cash from Bill and Dolly got her through Christmas and the New Year, but she began to wonder what would happen in a couple of weeks when the well ran dry. Lillian and Olive would help out of course. But wasn't she supposed to be provided for in Douggie's absence? She might hate Frank Skinner, but she couldn't survive without him.

Her first visit to see Douggie wasn't due until mid-February and until then she had only his brief letters to keep her going:

Its alrite in here really, ive got some mates already and the screws in our blok are quite nise, one of them gave me a sigar when Ronnie was born. All the paddys in here did there nut about that bloody sunday bisness so its really noisy. Food fucking terrible, could murder a pint. Remember that I love you and our kids and I think about you evry day. I really wont to go to bed with you Rita, I miss your luvly tits. Wear your nise bra when you come to see me.

★

Rita tried to write back with good news, but early in February the government declared a state of emergency and power cuts for up to nine hours were making life difficult. Apart from a gas fire in the front room, all the other heaters and the hot water were done on the electric and Rita was finding it hard to get the washing dry, especially Ronnie's nappies. It was a lot of work keeping the other two entertained in the absence of telly. They'd played games by candlelight a few times, Monopoly and so forth, but once the novelty had worn off, they started complaining about not being able to play their records or do anything. She did her best to keep everybody's spirits up by taking all three of them down to the pub where Dolly had plenty of paraffin heaters and always found something for the kids to do.

Although she told herself it was just because the sun was shining, one Friday morning in early February, Rita threw open all the windows and gave the flat a good clean. When everything was spotless, she ran herself a bath and carefully washed her hair, rinsing it in vinegar to make it extra shiny. Afterwards she dressed in a short skirt and fluffy cardigan which buttoned down the front so she could feed Ronnie easily. Beneath her jumper she put on Douggie's favourite bra that opened at the front. Her best shoes were scuffed and needed to be heeled, but she wiped the patent leather carefully with Vaseline and polished them with a duster.

At half-past three as she walked towards Richard Atkins Infants' School to wait for Marilyn with Ronnie in his pram – a lovely navy blue Silver Cross, another delivery from John Lewis – there he was. To her knowledge, the only Jag in Stockwell and Brixton belonged to Bill and Dolly, but theirs was red and this one was racing green, its chrome sparkling through the midwinter gloaming.

He saw her in his rear-view mirror as she turned the corner, the great pram in front of her. As she drew closer, he knew she'd spotted him, so he climbed out of the car and tried to sound casual. 'Rita' – his voice betrayed by a slight wobble – 'how are you, love?'

'Don't "love" *me*.' Rita pushed past, feeling her face burn. She felt stupid and self-conscious for having dressed up. She heard the soft thud of the car door closing and his footsteps behind her. He had Blakeys on his heels. He drew level with her at the school gate and stood beside her silently with his hands in his pockets. She could smell him.

'You got the pram all right then. Did the cot arrive?'

'Thank you, it's lovely.' Rita's voice was quiet but the brittle tone wouldn't shift.

'Let me give you a lift back to the flat, Rita. I think we need to sort a few things out, it won't take more than half an hour.' His voice was steady now, reasonable.

'I suppose so.' Rita's knuckles were white on the bar of the pram. They stood quietly for another minute or so until they heard the bell ring and the excited escapees came spilling out of the school doors. Marilyn was always one of the first out and today she was with her friend Linda, satchels flying behind them as they raced to the gates. Marilyn didn't seem surprised to see Frank.

'Hello, Frank, have you come to take us home in your nice car?'

'All right babe?' He pulled her ponytail gently. 'Jump in the front, then.'

Frank helped Rita separate the carriage of the pram from the carrycot. She kept her head down, avoiding his eyes, and carefully slid Ronnie across the long leather seat in the back. Frank folded the carriage and placed it gently in the boot.

Rita felt a thrill as he turned the key and the big, soft engine purred into life. She sat up straight and leaned an elbow on the leather arm-rest as the car glided powerfully away from the school, careful to avoid the eyes of the other waiting mothers staring into the car. Marilyn wittered on in the front, turning round on her knees to look at her brother in the back. 'Miss Vale says if I stop wiping my snot on my sleeve and take a hanky to school every day she'll give me a yellow star.' Rita smiled. Frank asked Marilyn what she was up to at school.

'Well, I was milk monitor until Miss Vale caught me and Gary Spall kissing under the table last week.'

'What are you doing kissing the boys, you little minx?' Frank laughed and tickled the back of her legs. Marilyn bubbled on: 'He gave me some Pontefract cakes, you know those soft black sweets. Anyway, Gary is my boyfriend, he asked Linda to ask if I loved him and she reckons he's nice so I said yes.'

Rita couldn't help herself and had to laugh out loud. Frank's brown eyes looked into her own green ones in the rear-view mirror and she allowed herself a shy smile.

'No point having a boyfriend unless he gives you things, Marilyn. Ain't that right, Rita?'

'That's right love, take 'em for everything.' Rita raised a sardonic eyebrow in the mirror and Frank grinned back at her. He had lovely teeth, Frank. She was beginning to enjoy herself.

Frank parked the car in the alley and helped Rita up the stairs with the pram. While she put the kettle on and changed Ronnie, Frank took Marilyn to the sweet shop next door. 'Don't give her too many sweets Frank, she won't eat her tea.' Her plea was lost in the excited sound of feet rushing down stairs and the slamming of the door.

She changed Ronnie and put his old nappy to soak in the bucket, then moved it into the bathroom, out of sight. Frank came back from the shop alone.

'Where's Marilyn?' Rita asked anxiously. Frank laughed and stood swaying with his hands in his pockets. If only he didn't look so relaxed, thought Rita, I might be able to calm down.

'She's downstairs in the alley. I bought her a skipping rope. She's fine.'

'Oh, OK then. Sugar?'

'No thanks.' Frank patted his flat stomach: 'Got to watch me figure.' He eased himself on to the sofa, pulling up the legs of his trousers as he sat. He leaned back, his legs wide apart, the hair on his legs showing between his socks and trousers, his hands stretched back behind his head. 'What time's Steve back?' Frank checked his watch.

'Not till half-past four. He does five-a-side after school on a Friday.' Rita put Frank's mug of tea on the arm of the settee closest to him and sat in the armchair opposite. She crossed one leg tightly over the other. Frank didn't try to hide the long slow gaze from her shoes to her face. Rita cleared her throat.

'So what did you arrange exactly with Douggie?'

'That I'd look after you.' He looked a little too pleased with himself for Rita's liking.

'What exactly does that involve?' She kept her voice steady.

'Well, money of course—'

'Of course,' Rita interrupted.

'Look Rita, I just want to make sure you don't go short, give you everything you need.'

'Except Douggie.' Frank could more than take care of her money worries, but as far as Rita was concerned, he would always owe her. Douggie might be able to forgive and forget, but it wasn't in her nature. She could nurse a grudge for years.

Frank stood up and paced around the tiny flat. He stopped by Ronnie's carrycot and tenderly brushed the baby's little cheek with a long finger. Rita held her breath. Frank turned suddenly and spoke.

'When was the last time you had a night out?'

Rita tried to remember. 'What, a proper night out, getting

legless, you mean? Blimey, must have been around the time I fell with Ronnie, probably the night I fell with Ronnie, almost a year then.'

'Get a babysitter for tomorrow night.' He wasn't asking. He fished in his pockets and pulled out a roll of cash, peeling off some notes and placing them carefully in Ronnie's carry-cot. 'And get yourself something nice to wear. Treat yourself. We're going out on the town.' Rita fought an urge to tell him to stick it up his arse but she'd seen a lovely aqua-marine dress with chiffon sleeves in the Bon Marché on Brixton High Road.

Marilyn's heavy step came crashing up the stairs and she burst in demanding: 'I'm starving, Mum, how long's tea?'

Frank slipped his jacket on. 'I'd better be pushing off, let you get on. See you tomorrow night then, about eight o'clock.' Rita nodded. She walked him down the stairs and opened the door, half hiding behind it. He hesitated on the doorstep, turning to leave then suddenly twisting back. Placing a hand behind her neck he pulled her lips briefly to his before sprinting down the stairs two at a time.

Or Has Time Rewritten Every Line?
1972 – Part Two

A nd so the pattern was set. Frank had organised it so that every Saturday evening an agency babysitter would arrive at the flat above the greengrocer's at 7 p.m. Power cuts were still making life difficult and on one occasion Rita had refused to go out and leave the babysitter to grope her way around a flat she didn't know with·the aid only of candles. She didn't like to leave the children with strangers, but to use either of the grandmothers or her sister would have invited unfavourable comment.

It was common knowledge that Frank was 'taking care' of Rita, but there was no need to flaunt the fact that she went dancing up the Locarno and the Talk of the Town while Douggie languished in Parkhurst. The children seemed to accept it as perfectly normal that their mum went dancing with Frank Skinner on a Saturday night – she and Douggie had hardly been stay-at-home types – but Rita would sometimes catch Steven looking quizzically at Frank from the corner of his eye. Marilyn, on the other hand, was easily bought with the gifts that came with their mother's dancing companion and could be mollified with the promise of a visit to see her dad soon.

Rita's first visit to Parkhurst came in the middle of February. Frank had tried to insist on driving her, but she was adamant that she would take the train to Portsmouth and then the ferry across to the Isle of Wight alone. It was a long day with a baby, but she preferred it that way. Frank had been the perfect gentleman and except for that one occasion on her doorstep hadn't laid a finger on her. All the same, she felt guilty and preferred a martyr's journey to visit her husband in prison. It seemed more appropriate somehow. She dressed up in her fluffy cardigan, short skirt and Douggie's favourite bra for her visit, though by the time she arrived Ronnie had dribbled all down her front.

If Rita was looking tatty Douggie didn't notice. Occasionally on family visits inmates were allowed a private room with a warden in attendance. Rita was led into a room with a table, four chairs and nothing else and sat for ten minutes waiting for the husband she'd last seen led away months ago. When he came in Rita and the baby burst out crying at the same time. 'Aren't you pleased to see me, then?' joked Douggie, pretty watery himself. He didn't know which to hold first, his wife or his son, so enfolded them both in his arms, crushing the baby and allowing Rita to sob into his shoulder.

'He's the dead spit of you, everybody says so.' Rita handed Douggie the baby.

'He's a big boy, ain't he?' Douggie beamed, feeling the weight of his new son.

'Yeah, he's bigger than all the other babies down at the clinic. Midwife says she's never known a kid like it for feeding. He's much greedier than the other two were.'

They had only half an hour together but even so there were lots of pauses in the conversation. They tried to keep it light and crack jokes but it was a miserable visit. While the warden pretended to be absorbed in the racing form in his paper, Rita undid her bra and latched the baby on, but it was more for Douggie's benefit and as he reached over to stroke the baby's head he squeezed her breast and looked deep into her eyes. Under the table his hands played around Rita's knees and he tried to make lewd comments but Rita knew it was all he could do to stop himself from crying. It came as something of a relief when the half hour was up.

On the ferry back to Portsmouth she wondered if it wouldn't be easier if they didn't see each other at all until he came home. It just got everyone upset having such short visits. She dreaded the next visit in a month's time when she was to take Steve and Marilyn with her. They'd be maudlin for weeks after seeing their dad.

Douggie had been pleased to hear that Frank was keeping an eye on the family and was delighted that Rita had even been taken dancing: 'That's great, love, you need to get out and let your hair down, stuck indoors with three kids all day.' She didn't mention that she'd been dancing every weekend and embellished slightly by saying that Dolly had accompanied them as part of a group. She faltered slightly when Douggie asked if Frank's wife Doreen went dancing with them. Not only had she not been dancing; her name hadn't even been mentioned.

Rita had wanted to bring it up and so the following Saturday as she and Frank sped in a cab towards the West End she asked: 'Doesn't Doreen fancy coming out? It would be nice to see her again.'

'She doesn't really like going out any more. Ever since she had the boys she's been the same. She says she's tired after working in the salon all week, but I think she prefers her own company most of the time.'

'Oh, I see. She's all right though, is she?' Rita tried to keep her tone light.

'Face like a wet weekend. But yeah, I suppose she's all right,' said Frank.

'Well, give her my love, won't you.'

'Sure.' They fell silent for a few moments, Rita practising in her head the question she wanted to ask, but not quite finding the courage. Just as the cab pulled up outside the Talk of the Town she blurted it out:

'Does Doreen know you take me out on a Saturday?'

'No.' Frank fished in his pockets for a note to pay the cab driver. He held the door open while Rita climbed out with small steps, careful not to show more of herself than was already visible in her short dress.

'Why not? Where do you tell her you're going?'

'Let's get inside and have a drink, shall we.'

With one hand gently on her back Frank guided Rita to the front of the queue that had formed. The doorman pulled back the rope around the doorway and let them through. The crowd stared enviously, wondering who they were. They didn't pay. Rita felt mucky. She had suspected, even hoped, that Frank kept their Saturday assignations a secret. She felt awful now that she knew.

Once inside, Rita toddled off to the ladies' powder room to check the elaborate 'do' that she'd fixed that afternoon at the hairdresser's. Her chestnut hair was piled up high on her head and fixed by a velvet ribbon, with ringlets hanging down the sides. Around her neck she wore a matching black velvet choker with a cameo. Her dress was cut low in an empire line and the short chiffon skirt moved fluidly as she walked. Her skin was scrubbed and shining, yet she felt grubby. The memory of Douggie's face earlier in the week added a sting. She resolved to have it out with Frank when she got back to their table. She didn't like all this creeping around like she was having an affair or something. She'd done nothing to be ashamed of and wasn't going to hide.

He'd chosen a table in the club's upper tier, used mostly for diners. It was quieter than the downstairs bar area and full mostly with couples who could watch the livelier goings-on beneath them from their balcony seats. The drapes were heavy red velvet, the walls a deep turquoise blue with copper-coloured fittings, and the carpet thick. Little lamps burning dim lights sat on each table. As Rita pushed open the door of the ladies', she spotted him and stood still for a few seconds. She had never seen him alone, in repose like this –

head bent down looking at his hands, brow slightly furrowed as if he was thinking hard. The white of his collar stood out sharply against the darkness of his suit and hair, his olive skin glowing in the low light. He looked sad and incredibly handsome.

She took a deep breath and pulling herself up ramrod straight walked slowly over to the table, conscious of every step and movement she made. As she neared him he seemed to sense her presence and looked up admiringly. Just before she reached the table, a waiter arrived with a bottle of champagne, two glasses and an ice-bucket. He pulled out Rita's chair for her and Frank stood up slightly as she sat down. It all seemed so formal that Rita felt unsure of herself. Douggie would never open doors or stand up for her and she felt curiously unsure of how to behave. 'Pull yourself together, you're a married woman with three kids,' she told herself.

Her resolve to tough it out faltered momentarily and as Frank raised his glass to clink her own she giggled for no reason. He scratched around his collar and loosened his tie a little. 'Look Rita,' he said, 'the reason I haven't said anything to Doreen is because we haven't really been talking to each other lately.' Rita was shocked.

'Why for God's sake?' She drew hard on a cigarette. She couldn't imagine it.

'Because I had an affair.'

'Oh.' She looked at him steadily, a little put out. 'Why?'

'Oh, I don't know, Rita. Why does anyone have an affair? Because you can, I suppose.'

'Are you still . . .?' She gulped back a big mouthful of champagne and had to swallow a burp.

'No, course not.' He sounded irritable.

'Well don't get all touchy. You were the one who said you'd been seeing someone else.'

'She was just some little tart who used to hang around the card school, she didn't mean anything. None of them do.'

He moistened the end of a cigar with his lips.

'What do you mean "none of them"? How many are there?' Rita's eyes widened.

'Don't be naive, Rita, you know how many women there are that like to fuck villains. They get a kick out of it. They make me sick, if you must know.'

'I'm sure nobody twists your arm, Frank. You don't have to do it.' She drained her glass and Frank refilled it before he spoke.

'I'm no different to any other man, Rita. If it's offered to me on a plate, I take it. We're all the same.'

'Douggie's not.' Rita was indignant.

'No, you're right. Douggie's not like that.' He stared at her face, taking in the softness of its contours and the sharp liveliness in her eyes. 'But then again, Douggie's got you.' Rita coloured.

'So? You've got Doreen.'

'Yeah, but I don't love Doreen.'

'So why did you marry her, for Christ's sake?'

'Because you married Douggie.' He looked down at the cigar he was fingering before levelling his gaze at her face. She trembled and lit another cigarette. 'I'd have killed for you, Rita.'

'You almost did, that was the trouble.'

'Jesus Christ, Rita, I was a kid. All young blokes get into fights.' His face reddened.

'You almost killed that poor bloke, Frank, and all because we had a dance together. He was sixteen, Frank, *sixteen*.' Rita crossed one leg over the other and started to swing it nervously.

'You're telling me that you packed me in because of one fight?'

'It was a bit more than a fight, Frank, and you know it. I almost threw up when I saw what you'd done to him. He was in hospital for four months. How *could* you have?'

'Everyone gets into scrapes, Rita. Besides, I sorted his old girl out for cash, no harm done.' He shrugged nonchalantly.

'Yeah well, that's typical of you. You think money makes everything all right.'

'You didn't give me a fucking chance. One minute we were courting heavy, all happy, then six months later you go and get married to that dopey cunt.'

Frank put the cigar to his mouth and was about to light it when Rita's outstretched palm flew across the table, sending the lighter flying and breaking the cigar in half. She only grazed his mouth, but he got the message. Raising his hands in a gesture of surrender, he said, 'All right, all right, I'm sorry. I didn't mean it. He's not a cunt, he's a good bloke.'

'Good enough to save your bloody neck,' Rita spat.

For several moments they fell quiet, Rita looking pinched. Frank sighed and ran his hands through his hair. 'The truth is, Rita, I haven't got a fucking soul in the world I can trust. And I look at you and Douggie, the way you are with him and the kids, and I wonder how different it could have been with you. You're a good woman, Rita, you're beautiful, decent and you don't take shit from no one. I want someone like you.'

'You've got one at home. Why don't you just go back and make it up with her?' As she said it, she hoped he wouldn't.

'I'm always going to look after Doreen and the boys but we'll never be close. She can't be a friend to me like you were 'cause she needs me too much. She's not in your league.' A large smile spread across his features. 'Do you remember how much we used to muck about all the time? You were such a laugh. And I could really talk to you, even then when we were kids.'

'Yeah, only 'cause I wouldn't let you get in my knickers. We had to do something.'

'True.' They both chuckled. Frank drained the bottle into their glasses and waved to the waiter for another. He burst out laughing at some memory that flashed across his mind. Rita smiled at him, waiting for an explanation.

'What?'

'I was just thinking of the time we had that row in a cab outside that club in Tooting when I told you to wait because I had to go inside and do a bit of business. Do you remember?'

'Oh yeah, you had all those bags full of knocked-off clobber.'

'So I gets out the cab and says, "Shut up and stay there!" What do you do, little cow, but chuck all the gear out the window of the cab then get out and start shouting the odds as you're walking off down the road. So I grabs you, opens the door of the cab and shoves you inside, and you bloody well open the door on the other side and get out . . .' Frank was bent over now, barely able to breathe for laughter, tears in his eyes. 'And then you go up to that copper and tell him that I'm giving you grief and he bloody well tries to arrest me. I could have killed you.'

'I don't even remember what the row was about.' Rita's eyes were glazed, the champagne and good humour warming her face, her smile radiant.

'No, neither do I, but I remember running all the way over to your mum's in Clapham and when I get there, you leaning out the window and abusing me. I never took crap from anyone the way I used to take it from you.'

Frank reached over, took her hand and squeezed it. She didn't pull away. 'I was mad about you, Rita.' His voice was soft, his dark brown eyes shining.

'We were kids, Frank, it was a long time ago.'

'I know. Be my friend, Reet, I need someone to talk to.' She squeezed his hand until her knuckles went white and then leaned across the table and kissed him. He smiled and said, 'Come 'ere you' and pulled her roughly on to his lap, where he squeezed her tightly. 'You smell lovely Rita. You always did. You've got such sweet skin.' He gazed at her cleavage. 'You're bigger than you used to be.' She slapped him playfully. 'Cheeky sod, I'm full of milk, I've got a new baby.' She eased herself off his lap, but pulled her chair closer so they sat with their arms touching.

'You get better looking with every kid, don't you? Most women go to seed.' Frank appraised her fully and stroked her stomach. 'The day I came into the pub just before you had Ronnie you looked so gorgeous, I wanted to fuck you there and then.' Rita opened her mouth to protest but no words came out. She felt aroused despite herself. She linked her fingers through his and stroked his hand. She'd forgotten what lovely hands he had. Long tapered fingers that looked like they'd never done a day's work in their life. She looked at his cuticles and wondered if he had manicures. With his free hand, he stroked her back gently; so lightly that she got goosebumps, little hairs raised up on her arms and legs, poking through her sheer tights.

When the waiter passed, Frank thrust a bundle of notes at him. 'Can I pay up, mate? Bring us another bottle, unopened to take away . . .' The waiter had a full tray and bustled past barely acknowledging him. Frank clenched his jaw and as the waiter made his way back along their tier towards another table to take an order, Frank grabbed his arm roughly and said, 'I told you I wanted to pay up.' The waiter tried to shake his arm free but Frank's knuckles were white and he had him in a vice.

'Other people have been waiting longer than you.' The waiter's words were bold, but there was a tremble in his voice.

'Leave it, Frank,' Rita commanded and Frank let him go, but not without a murderous look that would leave him in no doubt what would happen if he didn't come back with another bottle double quick.

'What did you do that for? Poor bloody sod, he's rushed

off his feet.' Rita looked at Frank's profile and could tell he was grinding his teeth.

'I don't like being ignored.'

Frank hailed a taxi outside the Talk of the Town and with his hand around Rita's waist, pushed her gently inside. As they moved steadily southwards towards her flat, he held her and stroked her face and neck, kissing her all the while. She'd never slept with Frank while they were courting – though she'd often wanted to – and had forgotten what a sexy man he was. She tried not to compare him to Douggie and shut her husband out of her mind, but he was clumsy compared to Frank. She felt disloyal, but not enough to stop him. By the time the cab pulled up outside the flat, Frank had removed her knickers and tights and thrown them out of the window. She had a wobbly moment when the knickers came off and felt suddenly shy: 'I'm not back to normal yet, Frank, I only had the stitches out a couple of weeks ago.'

Grabbing her hair and pulling her head backwards he told her, 'Shut up, Rita, I don't care. I love you.'

In the flat, Rita went straight into the bathroom, embarrassed to let the babysitter see her bare legs. Frank paid the woman and saw her out, knocking gently on the bathroom door on his way back up the stairs. Rita had taken her hair down, the pins scattered in the sink, the chestnut curls tumbling around her shoulders. She hid her nakedness behind the door and he stroked her face:

'God, look at you, you're fucking lovely. Are you sure you want to do this?'

'Just let me check on the kids. Go into the bedroom, I'll be in in a minute.'

Frank crept away at 6 a.m. before the children woke up and Rita lay in bed holding the pillow with his scent on it close to her. When Ronnie cried, she pulled him out of his cot and before suckling him, washed herself with a flannel. She gazed down at her son, so like his dad, and searched for feelings of guilt that wouldn't come. Her abiding memory was of Frank's face and how he'd whispered, 'I've waited fifteen years to do that' when his breathing finally slowed. Rita looked at her perfect son and tried to squash the thought that she'd married the wrong man.

The days passed slowly. She hoped he might pop in during the week, but no word came and she steeled herself to sit tight until Saturday night rolled round again. She was so happy she felt miserable and on Wednesday when Dolly came round for a drink, Rita told all.

'Well girl, I think you're mad, but I suppose you've got a history with him. Just don't get your hopes up, Rita, you know what he's like deep down. He might say he loves you, but he's a bad lot and he'll never change. If he's fucked around on Doreen he'll do the same to you eventually. Quite apart from the fact that he's a vicious bastard. There was a good reason you didn't marry him in the first place.' Dolly was firm.

'Yeah, but Doll, I can't tell you how he made me feel. I've only ever slept with Douggie, I had no idea how different it could be. I thought all men were the same.'

Dolly, more worldly, smiled at Rita's innocence. 'Douggie's a good man, Reet, he really loves you. You can't put a price on that. I know he's not smooth like Frank but he's a diamond. You've got a good marriage and it would break his heart if he ever found out. You know how trusting he is.'

'I know, I know.' Rita paused, her thoughts elsewhere. 'But Dolly, Frank's so gentle, he's nothing like you think he'd be. He treated me like a queen, I thought I was going to wake the kids up. He kissed me, you know, down there.' She nodded down at her lap. 'Douggie's never done that. I felt really shy at first and tried to stop him, but he was at it for ages. It was beautiful, Doll.'

'Be careful, Rita.'

'Oh no, it's all right, they stuck me on the pill at the clinic last month when I had the stitches out. Said it would help my heavy periods.'

'I didn't mean that.' Dolly fixed her in the eye. 'Careful how you are with him around the kids. They're not bloody silly these days, they catch on quick, not like when we were little.'

'Mmm.' Rita drifted off. When Dolly left at ten o'clock she felt pissed off. Of course Dolly was right, but she'd never felt like this. She loved Douggie, but he'd never made love to her the way Frank had. Oh, he was keen in the bedroom, but a bit rough and she was always glad when he'd finished. In twelve years of marriage she'd never refused him. Even when he came staggering in in the middle of the night reeking of drink and pulled up her nightie she went along with it to make him happy.

After what seemed like an age, Saturday night finally came around. The babysitter arrived on the dot of seven and Rita spent longer than usual getting herself made up. She'd made the kids take their bath early so she had more time to concentrate on herself. Usually she'd still be running around getting crisps and bottles of Coke for the kids and sorting out the aerial on the telly when Frank arrived, but that night she was ready at ten-past eight and pacing the flat. When he didn't arrive on the dot of half-eight she told herself to calm down. He was probably caught up somewhere. He'd get a message to her if it was off. She didn't have a phone, but he could always call the pub and they'd tell her of any changes. Nine o'clock rolled around and still no Frank. She started getting snappy and shouting at the kids, finally packing them off to bed at half-nine. By ten o'clock there was still no sign. Finally at 10.30 she let the babysitter go. She waited up till midnight, then gave it up as a bad job and fell into bed where she cried herself to sleep.

The next day she was due at Olive's for Sunday lunch with the kids. On her way to the bus stop, she called in at the Angel to ask Dolly if there had been any messages. Dolly looked at her, concerned: 'What's the matter, love?'

'He didn't show last night, Doll.'

'I told you, didn't I? He's a fucking bastard.' Dolly slammed a pint pot down on the bar.

'No, Doll, something must have happened. He wouldn't have let me down.'

'Are you sure, Rita? Don't you think now he's got what he wanted he'll piss off?'

'You just don't know him the way I do.'

'Know who?' Marilyn was listening carefully to her mother's conversation.

'Never mind, Marilyn. Do your coat up, come on, we're going.'

'Rita, love.' Dolly looked at her friend imploringly. 'I'm sorry, I'm sure you're right, I just worry about you, that's all.'

'Never mind eh, it doesn't matter. Pop round later, yeah?' Rita was doing up her children's coats and tying their scarves tight around their necks, marshalling them towards the door.

Lunch at Olive's was fraught. The children, picking up on their mother's mood, were fractious and behaved badly. Steve sat in front of the telly the whole time even when Olive switched it off; Marilyn refused to eat her dinner. 'Come on, Marilyn, eat your bloody dinner. It's best beef,' ordered Olive.

'I don't bloody like beef,' the child retorted. Rita slapped her and told her not to be rude to her nan. 'She's an old cow, you said so the other day,' Marilyn shot back before running off to cry her eyes out and pour a whole bottle of Dot down the toilet. This sent Olive into a fit of rage and when she slapped Marilyn's legs, Rita got on her high horse. 'Keep your dirty great hands off my kids,' she told her mother-in-law.

'If you can't control them, Rita, maybe they ought to come and live with me. I'd soon knock a bit of sense into them.' Olive stacked the plates noisily.

'Over my dead body,' said Rita furiously and ordered the kids to get their coats on. 'Come on you lot, we're going, I've had enough.'

'I haven't finished my trifle, Mum,' complained Steve.

'Do as you're told, Steven.'

Rita cried all the way home on the bus. Marilyn, thinking it was all her fault, kept saying over and over, 'I'm sorry, Mum, I didn't mean to pour all Nan's Dot down the loo. It just fell out.'

'It's not you, stupid,' Steve said. 'She's crying because her boyfriend didn't turn up last night.' Rita, too upset to reprimand her son, just cried some more.

'Shut up you div, Mum's boyfriend is Dad.' Marilyn kicked her brother and pandemonium broke loose. By the time they got off the bus all four of them were red-faced with tears streaming down their faces. The baby howled and wriggled in Rita's arms. As they reached the front door, Dolly was coming towards them down the road.

'Dear Lord, what's happened here then?' soothed Dolly.

'I can't handle it any more, Dol. Sodding kids are driving me round the bend.'

Rita stormed up the stairs and shut her screaming infant in the bedroom before she throttled him. Dolly ordered Rita into the bath and got out the Monopoly board while the kettle boiled. 'Right then you two, come and sit down and play nicely. If you can't, you can go to bed.' Worried now by the sight of their sobbing mother and the sound of their howling baby brother, Marilyn and Steve sat sullenly playing.

'Why is Mum crying, Dolly?' asked Steve.

'Because you made her, you div,' offered Marilyn.

'Shut up the pair of you or you can both go to bed. I mean it.' Dolly waved a finger menacingly at their faces. 'Your mum's not well, Steve, she's just a bit run down, that's all. Anyway, you're not helping by arguing, just try and keep quiet for a few minutes while I take her in a cup of tea.'

Dolly knocked gently on the bathroom door and let herself in. Rita had stopped crying, but was lying inert in the water, all the life drained out of her. 'Is it worth it, Rita? Look at the state of you.'

'How could I be so stupid, Doll? I thought he loved me.' Slowly Rita began to soap herself.

'Yeah well, never mind eh? We all make mistakes. Just make sure you get your money off him and leave it at that. You should arrange for him to bring the cash in to me; that way you don't have to see him at all. It'll be better in the end, love.'

Rita sniffed and nodded, exhausted and defeated. She stepped out of the bath, half dried herself and pulled on her quilted dressing gown. Down the hallway Ronnie screamed.

'I'd better go and feed that baby. Poor little sod.'

That night when the children had been put to bed, Rita sat on the settee smoking and looking at the telly without really taking it in. She fished around in the drawers until she found some paper and an envelope and started writing a letter to Douggie. She felt so ashamed. If it wouldn't have hurt him so much, she'd have liked to tell Douggie how stupid she'd been, but instead wrote a cheerful note saying how the kids were as good as gold and what a lovely time they'd had at his mum's that day. She pressed the kids' school uniforms and put their dinner money into little brown envelopes. She washed up the cups and plates, packed away the Monopoly and wiped down the surfaces. She was just about to turn the lights out and go to bed when there was an urgent banging on the door. Looking at the clock on the kitchen wall she saw that it was quarter-past eleven. Who on earth was waking the house up at this time of night?

He looked terrible. His face was drawn and even in the lamplight from the street she could see that he was pale.

'What do you want? It's the middle of the night, the kids are in bed . . .'

'Please let me in, Rita, I'm in trouble.' His voice was trembling and he seemed unsteady on his feet. She widened the door to let him through and followed him up the stairs. He slumped on the sofa, breathing heavily.

'What's the matter?' she asked sharply.

'Oh Christ, Rita . . .' He was shaking now: his head collapsed into his hands and he began to sob.

'What happened? Hold on, I think there's a drop of Scotch in the cupboard left over from Christmas. No one saw you coming here, did they?' He shook his head. She poured him a large glass, which he downed in one. She refilled it for him and perched on the arm of the chair waiting for him to speak. He remained silent.

'Are you going to tell me what's going on, or am I supposed to sit here all night?'

Taking a deep breath and in a faltering voice, he began to speak: 'I did a job with Barry Gill on Friday. We followed a jeweller from Hatton Garden to his drum in Highgate. It should have been really easy, but the fucking Yid must have sensed us there when he got out of the car and started shouting his head off and running towards his front door. I don't know why, but I panicked and Barry got in my way and I ended up shooting him instead. It was a mistake, I didn't mean to. I got the case off the old boy and bundled Barry into the car . . .' His face was contorted.

'Where's Barry now? Hospital?' Rita's heart was almost coming out of her mouth. She hated guns.

'No, no, no, of course not.'

'What do you mean? Where is he?'

'Kent.'

'Kent? What's he doing in Kent?' Rita's voice rose.

'I took him there today.'

'Why didn't you take him to the hospital?'

'How could I? They'd have asked questions, I couldn't.'

Bile rose in her throat. She knew before she asked what the answer would be: 'Well, who's he with, is he all right?'

'No he's not all right, Rita. He's dead. I buried him under a pylon near Sittingbourne.'

After a couple more Scotches he calmed down sufficiently to run through the events of the weekend in more detail. He'd shot Barry in the groin as he'd attempted to wrestle the jeweller to the ground. The jeweller made so much noise that Frank pumped two bullets from a sawn-off shotgun into his head at close range to shut him up. He bundled his friend into the car and then drove him to a lock-up garage under the arches in Vauxhall. They arrived at about 7 p.m. on the Friday evening, but it took until the early hours of Sunday morning for Barry Gill, slumped in the back of their stolen car, to bleed to death. During that time Frank had not left the garage and had sat silently on a stool in the corner of the lock-up enduring the moans of his friend begging to be taken to hospital. When he was quite sure that life had been drained from the body, he threw an old dustsheet around it and bundled the corpse into the boot. Rita sat silently and listened to him, all the colour gone from her face. It was inconceivable that this was the same man that had been in her bed a week ago.

Frank explained that he had driven east out of London and into Kent. He drove slowly around the Kent countryside and finally decided on the embankment alongside the A2 near Sittingbourne. Off it was a works sliproad which the police wouldn't venture down even if they were to be driving past on the off-chance. It was about 6 a.m. by the time Frank dragged the body from the car and 300 yards into the field where the line of pylons ran. With about an hour before it became light he dug into the frozen ground, adrenalin pumping through his exhausted body. It took forty minutes to bury the body deep enough for it not to be traced by dogs. He piled the earth into the grave, pausing only to glance at the wedding ring on his friend's finger. It was then that he threw up, retching again and again, his empty stomach bringing up nothing but bile.

Shaking, he got back into the stolen car and drove it slowly to the lock-up in Vauxhall. He parked in the alley round the back and went inside only long enough to remove all his clothing, change into overalls and douse the blood-sodden clothes in petrol. Then he threw them into the boot of the car, above the petrol tank, before setting a match to it and running the half mile to his own car which he'd left parked in Kennington Lane on the Friday afternoon. He drove back to his house in Clapham where he bathed and changed before his wife or sons woke up.

Used to his absences and still not really speaking to him, Doreen didn't bother to ask where he'd been since Friday. She cooked a Sunday lunch and was surprised that he didn't go straight out afterwards, but sat with the boys Mark and Craig watching the big match on the telly before taking them down the park to kick a ball about.

Only when the phone rang that night at 10.30 did Frank begin to lose his composure. Doreen shouted down the stairs: 'Frank! It's Karen on the phone, she wants to know if you've seen Barry.' Calmly, he picked up the downstairs extension and explained to Barry Gill's wife that he'd seen him on Friday lunchtime in the pub, but not since. He even managed to share a joke with her before placing the phone back on its cradle: 'Never mind, love, he'll turn up when the pub finally throws him out.' Without looking back or saying anything to his wife, Frank Skinner picked up his jacket and keys and walked out the front door.

Rita sat like a stone, her face impassive. Frank looked at her, waiting.

'Why did you have to tell me, Frank?'

'I had to Rita, I was going mad.' He reached out a hand to stroke her leg, which she drew away, repulsed.

'What about his family, what are you going to tell them?'

'Nothing.'

'Nothing! That poor woman's got to spend the rest of her life wondering what happened to her husband?' Rita thought how easily it could have been Douggie.

'What choice have I got?' he asked. She stared at him, disbelief and hatred in her eyes.

'Rita, don't turn on me, what else could I do? I've never killed anyone before.' He was begging her now, desperate.

'Oh well that makes it all right then.' Rita was composed. 'Get out, Frank. You leave my money with Dolly on a Monday, but you never come near me or my kids and if you ever try to get in touch with Douggie again I'll be straight down the police station. Understand?'

'Rita, please . . .'

'Go, Frank.' She turned her back on him and stood leaning over the sink, her knuckles turning white on the draining board. She heard him pick up his keys, but didn't turn round, just kept staring at the plug-hole. He moved quietly across the lounge and opened the door. Before walking through it he said:

'I'll come back and get you one day, Rita. You know it's me and you.'

CHAPTER EIGHT

A Day at the Races

Douggie came through the front door whistling, the sign of a good day at the car lot. Slinging his jacket over the banister he called out to Rita, who was in the back garden seeing to a few odds and sods that needed doing before dishing up the tea. He found her pulling the dead heads from the peonies, her favourite flower.

'All right babe?' Douggie kissed his wife's head and stretched out on one of the patio chairs.

'Yeah not bad. Want a beer?' Douggie smiled and lightly flicked her backside as she brushed past him into the kitchen.

'You're cheerful.' Douggie watched his wife as she handed him his beer. She sat in the chair next to his and began to dig out the dirt from under her nails with an old toothpick from her apron pocket.

'Yeah well, I love it out here this time of year, don't I?' She smiled broadly at him. 'I even caught Ronnie doing a bit of revision when I got back from work, but for Christ's sake don't let on. He wouldn't want us to think he was bothered about his exams.'

'When do they start?'

'Thursday afternoon his first one. He finishes in a couple of weeks.'

'He hasn't got anything on the fifth, has he?'

'I don't know, his timetable is in the kitchen somewhere. Why?'

'Frank's got a load of tickets for the Derby – Members' Stand. I thought it would be nice if we all went, make a day of it.' She faltered only slightly before answering.

'It's a Wednesday the Derby, isn't it? I suppose I could just close the shop, I'd only be doing a half-day anyway. Yeah, go on then, it'll be nice. We haven't been racing for ages.' Douggie smiled in agreement and thought better of mentioning his recent trips to Plumpton and Sandown.

The ease of summer had finally arrived at the Fisher household. Rita was beginning to think she could put down the aggravation of the last few months to her going through the change of life. There had been a lull in hostilities recently. Rita was becoming accustomed to Douggie's role at the club and, although she still couldn't face a visit, had been pleasantly surprised by the money he managed to pull out of it each week. He had taken to slipping the odd two hundred quid here and there into her knicker drawer: a tactic that never failed to keep her quiet. Douggie had said that they'd start stashing some soon, but they might as well just have a good summer and enjoy the extra cash for a while. Rita had been depositing little bits in the building society all the same.

She slipped a couple of fillet steaks under the grill and looked at the back of Douggie's head through the kitchen window. It bobbed slightly as he whistled, the thinning hairs at the back of the crown glowing in the sunlight. 'You know you have to wear a hat in the Members' Stand on Derby Day, don't you?' he called out.

'I'm not wearing a bloody hat. They look terrible at my age, like the mother of the bride.' She lowered a handful of chips into the deep-fat fryer.

'They won't let you in if you haven't got one on. I'll treat you. Go to Allders, get a good one.' Douggie paused to drain his can. 'Get us another beer while you're in there,' he said.

'I don't care, I'm not wearing one.' Rita handed him another can through the window.

'Well you'll have to sit in the bloody car park all day then, won't you.'

A fortnight later the sun rose bright and early on Derby Day and Rita and Douggie were sitting up in bed with cups of tea by 6.30. The paper boy had come early so Douggie was studying the racing form while Rita read the middle pages of the newspaper. Ronnie had been up for a couple of hours doing some last-minute revision before his final exam, O level geography, that morning. After several lively discussions, Douggie had relented and agreed to Ronnie staying on at John Kramer's to do A levels on the condition that he passed each and every one of his eight O levels. As the school only required potential sixth-formers to pass five, Ronnie had argued that his father was just being 'bloody-minded because I'm not doing what you want'. 'That's about the size of it,' his father had replied. They both knew that when it came to it Ronnie would get his own way no matter how many O levels he passed, but his father wanted to be seen to be exerting the last shreds of authority over his younger son.

All high days and holidays in the Fisher home started with a comprehensively huge breakfast. By 7.30 Douggie was in the kitchen frying sausages and rashers of bacon which were sizzling so loudly that he had to turn the radio up to hear 'Hit Me with Your Rhythm Stick', his favourite song of the moment. Rita was sitting in the garden enjoying her first cigarette of the day while Ronnie stomped around looking for his school tie.

'You're off to school early, aren't you?' bellowed Douggie.

'I'm going to sit in the library. It's too noisy to do any work round here.'

'Oh belt up, you always do your homework with your records blaring. Come on, sit down and have a bit of breakfast.'

'I'm not hungry, Dad.'

'Well you better eat something, there's going to be plenty of drinking later, I don't want you throwing up.' Douggie cracked two eggs into hot fat, their edges turning brown immediately. Ronnie grimaced at the spectacle of his father stooped over the spitting pan and stepped into the garden.

'Mum, have you seen my tie?'

'In the front room where you left it.' Rita exhaled slowly. 'You all right, love, bit nervous?' Ronnie scratched his crotch absent-mindedly.

'Yeah, a bit.'

'Never mind. It'll all be over in a couple of hours, then you can enjoy yourself, have a couple of bets, little drink.'

'What am I going to bet with? I haven't got any money.' The familiar refrain.

'Take twenty quid out of my purse and don't tell your father.'

'Cheers, Mum. Right, I'm off.'

'Give us a kiss then.' Ronnie bent and kissed his mother's cheek. 'Don't forget your badge for the Members' Stand or they won't let you in. We'll see you about noon in the bar.'

Douggie and Rita ate their breakfast in the garden, bickering happily about the day ahead to the accompaniment of birdsong and the low rumble of rush-hour traffic along Foxley Lane. Rita was unmoved by Douggie's repeated threats that she would not be let into the Members' Stand without a hat.

'Watch me,' she challenged. 'Right then, I'm going to have my bath before everybody starts turning up.' Within a couple of hours they would have a full house. They were meeting Frank, Doreen and Mark at the racecourse, and Marilyn, not yet awake after another rowdy evening in Croydon, was supposed to be going with them; Steve and Shelley were coming over from Norwood, Gully from Thornton Heath; they'd leave their cars at Douggie's and all take cabs. There were no designated drivers at a Fisher party. Everybody got pissed.

Five minutes before noon the entire gathering, save Ronnie, were gathered along the bar of the Members' Stand. All the women were topped in varying styles of millinery except for Rita who had coolly circumnavigated the issue by declaring, 'It blew off in the car park and ended up miles away' and marching ahead before the doorman checking passes and dress could protest. Frank kicked off the day by buying two bottles of Krug. Douggie, more of a mild-and-bitter man, blanched at the round-buying precedent set by his partner. Reading his thoughts, Rita turned to him.

'And don't you go buying champagne just to keep up with him,' she warned.

'Sixty quid a bottle,' he whispered.

'How much?' Rita screeched rhetorically. Doreen heard and cast her a pitying glance. Rita poked her tongue at the back of Doreen's freshly tinted platinum bob topped by a scarlet pillbox hat. Douggie laughed, 'Pack it in.'

The ensemble moved outside and pulled together two round tables on the terrace. Douggie came back from the toilet, beaming: 'That's made my day that has, I've just had a slash next to Hurricane Higgins!' Rita positioned herself between Douggie and Shelley at the far end of the two tables; the furthest possible point from Frank. Half-heartedly she struck up a conversation with Shelley about her work in the beauty salon and whether or not there might be an opening for Marilyn when she left college in three weeks. Absorbed in a study of Frank's profile, Rita paid scant attention to Shelley's replies. His permanent tan looked well against the white of his shirt and navy blue suit. He seemed at ease, cracking jokes with Steve and Gully about how much they could expect to lose that day. Shooting his cuff to check the time on his gold watch, he turned and saw Rita staring at him. He smiled. 'What time's your Ronnie coming?' he asked. Steve chimed in: 'Any minute now.'

Steve had seen his mother staring at Frank and gave her a funny look, which she turned away from. She gulped back the remainder of her drink and motioned to Douggie to pour her another.

'Go steady, we've only been here ten minutes, you're already on your third. It's not like you.' But Douggie refilled his wife's glass.

'It's a special occasion, so what if I fancy a drink?'

Douggie moved to the other end of the table, where Frank engaged him in a conversation about a refit at the club.

'Let's not talk shop eh Frank, it's a day out.'

Steve swapped places with his father and put an arm around Rita's shoulder. She smiled and leaned into his embrace, touching his hand.

'You all right Mum?'

'Yeah, why shouldn't I be?'

'No. You just look a bit far away that's all.'

'Oh, I'm all right, I was just wondering how that brother of yours got on this morning. Speak of the devil.' Ronnie came through the glass doors of the Members' Stand and out on to the terrace, slurping from a pint glass. Rita squinted up at his lanky form, her hand shielding her eyes from the sun. 'How did you get on?'

'Yeah, pissed it. No problem.'

'Charming. Grab a chair and sit down. Did you get a programme?' his mother asked.

Ronnie patted his pocket. Rita relaxed; she found the presence of her younger son inexplicably comforting. He was such a nice straightforward kid, really happy-go-lucky. The same could not be said of her daughter, whose chair was at a slight angle to the rest of the group. Her sunglasses masked her bloodshot eyes as she stared moodily ahead smoking a cigarette. Rita could tell she was feeling irritable by the way she was bouncing her crossed leg up and down with her foot half out of her shoe. Perhaps she was disappointed because Mark still hadn't shown up. There was no point trying to talk to her until she'd had enough drink to put the morning's hangover behind her.

Rita was surprised to see Doreen pull up a chair next to Marilyn and fall into friendly conversation. Neither of them had hitherto shown much interest in the other, though Marilyn might want to get in with Doreen because she had a soft spot for her son. Rita was intrigued by how much they seemed to have to say to one another. She was straining in an attempt to catch a snippet of their conversation, but they were talking in hushed tones, which piqued Rita's interest even more.

'Picked out your horses yet, Mum?' asked Steve.

'I've had a quick look, but the first race isn't until two o'clock, we've got loads of time.' She turned her chair to face her son and tried to look interested in the form he was explaining to her from his programme, but she kept casting glances in Marilyn's direction. Something was up.

Ten days before the Derby Marilyn had been sitting in the waiting room of the private doctor who prescribed her the amphetamines she had come to rely on to keep her weight down and her mood up. She preferred cocaine, but it wasn't always easy to come by and definitely beyond her means. Although the practice was a mere seventy-five yards from the family home in Foxley Lane, Marilyn knew she would never bump into anybody she knew, as Dr Dufty's surgery was attended almost exclusively by well-heeled housewives looking to adjust their attitudes or fend off the threat of their husbands' infidelity by keeping their bodies thin. There were never any men in the waiting room; Dr Dufty was a ladies' man.

Marilyn had been flicking through a magazine, waiting

impatiently to be called, when the glass patio doors of the surgery opened and through them came Doreen Skinner. At first Doreen didn't see Marilyn who was sitting in a recess just behind the door. It was only once she had checked in at reception and turned to find a seat that she saw her. Neither woman welcomed being recognised in Dufty's surgery because women only patronised his practice for the drugs their GPs would refuse to prescribe. He masqueraded as a medical practitioner who specialised in thyroid disorders. You only had to say you'd had a disturbed night's sleep or were feeling a bit tense because your thyroid was overactive, or lethargic because it was underactive, and the appropriate corrective could be collected at reception for a fee, on the way out.

Marilyn and Doreen looked at each other with the wry recognition of addicts. Although Doreen took a seat next to Marilyn, neither said why they were there – it was obvious. Doreen surmised correctly that Marilyn had probably come for speed, while Marilyn deduced from Doreen's vacant look that she was on some kind of tranquilliser or antidepressant, though her unusually slim figure might point to a bit of amphetamine abuse too.

'Long way for you to come, Doreen,' was Marilyn's opening gambit.

'Oh, I've been seeing him for seventeen years. It's a bit awkward now we've moved further out but once you find a doctor you get on with, you might as well stick with him. One of the stylists that used to work for me in the salon recommended him. He was wonderful to her when she had her first baby and got very down. Her own doctor just told her to pull her socks up, but Dufty was really sympathetic.'

'Mmm, he's very understanding.'

'Very.' Just then Marilyn's name was called and they said their goodbyes in a new-found spirit of camaraderie, each knowing that neither could tell on the other without giving the game away. Since that meeting, they had, like all addicts, felt especially drawn to each other and although they had nothing else in common, managed to chat easily for twenty minutes or so on the terrace until Frank interrupted them. 'Want another drink?'

It was a convenient moment for them to part and Doreen excused herself to go to the ladies' while Marilyn moved over to where her mother and Shelley were sitting.

'What were you two chatting about for all that time?' asked her mother.

'Nothing, just talking.' Rita nodded but looked at her daughter strangely. 'Don't start, Mum.'

Rita couldn't stand the idea of another of their little spats and so wandered inside to the tote where she placed bets on each of the seven races, choosing the horses by name rather than form. Her bets were modest for the most part, £2 each way and the odd fiver to win, though for the Derby itself she fancied Shahrastri and stuck an unprecedented £20 to win; at fourteen to one the odds were good. When she told Douggie and her sons they roared with laughter. 'No chance, Mother,' cried Ronnie. 'You'd have been better off giving the twenty quid to me.'

'I think you've had enough for one day.'

By the time the first race started Gully was very pissed, though Rita noticed with irritation that he hadn't actually put his hand in his pocket and bought a round. He was such a sponge, it drove her mad. 'Come on mate, let's walk you down to the finishing post so we can get a good look at my horse when it wins.' Douggie steered his weaving friend down the steps on to the course, followed by the rest of the group except for Rita who wanted to stay behind and keep their seats.

When Frank stepped out on to the terrace with more champagne he found her alone, looking a little dreamy. 'Penny for them,' he said.

Rita sat up with a start and her hand involuntarily flew to her hair, which she tried to smooth back over her ears.

'Oh, hello, I thought you'd gone down to the track with the others.'

'No, it's packed down there. I can't be bothered, you can see everything just as well from here.' He chuckled slightly to himself and wondered aloud, 'Funny, isn't it, everyone together again after all these years. It's like we drifted apart in the middle of our lives and now we've come back together at the end of it.' The Krug was making Frank philosophical.

'Don't talk like that. You make it sound as if our lives are over. I'm not fifty yet and you're not fifty-two until October.' Rita coloured a little to think that she still knew exactly when his birthday was, but turned to face him all the same. She loved a good discussion; it wasn't often she got the chance. The wind was picking up and blowing her hair in her face, she stopped trying to smooth it down.

'Well they are really, the best bits anyway – all the falling in love and having your kids and making your money bit has gone. Funny, innit? Seems only five minutes ago we had it all ahead of us.' Frank seemed easy with this realisation, but it plunged Rita into gloomy reflection. He was right. Ronnie would only be at home for a couple more years, then that was it, just work and Douggie. The thought was chilling. Seeing her face, Frank laughed. 'Don't get miserable about it, everybody's got to get old, Rita, we've had a good life. Well I'm presuming a bit.' He hesitated, then said, 'Would you say you're pleased with the way yours has turned out?' Frank looked at her while he refilled her glass.

'God, I haven't really thought about it. I suppose so. You're just so busy getting on with it, what with working and kids and everything. Why, are you pleased with the way yours turned out?'

'Well I've got plenty of dough, that's always nice, but I suppose I missed out in other areas.'

'Like what?' Rita wanted to know.

'Well, you know, personal like. I haven't always got what – or should I say who – I wanted.' Frank picked up her hand and looked at her wedding ring before laying it back on her lap. Rita gulped and wasn't sure if she was relieved or annoyed when Ronnie came up the steps from the track two at a time.

'Fucking old nag. Fifteen quid down the drain. Got any more money, Mum?'

'In my purse.' Rita tutted: 'And watch your language. Anyway what are you doing putting all your money on one horse? That was supposed to last you all day.'

'Spencer's dad had a tip. Supposed to be a dead cert.' He reached his oversized hands into her bag and pulled two twenties out of her purse. 'Nice one, Mum.'

'Put one of those back, that's my shopping money.'

''Ere you are son, put your mother's money back. Use this.' Frank leaned back in his chair and dug his hand into his pocket, retrieving a large roll of notes. He peeled off a fifty and handed it to Ronnie.

'Don't give him all that, Frank,' Rita said. But Ronnie was already making tracks towards the bookies at the edge of the course. 'Honestly Frank, you shouldn't have done, he'll only lose it. Just like his bloody father, only picks the ones that come in second.'

'No, he's all right. He's enjoying himself. Anyway, where were we? Oh yeah, life.' He smiled at her: 'What about you then – content?'

'Yeah,' said Rita equivocally,. 'I suppose so. We've got a lovely home, none of the kids are in trouble, touch wood, we're pretty healthy.' It didn't really sound enough to her, so she added, 'Douggie's a good husband.' She didn't look at Frank when she said it and scanned the railings for Douggie's familiar bald pate, hoping he wasn't on his way back. It didn't seem proper to be talking about him like this.

'He keeps you happy does he?'

'Yeah, of course, he's a good provider.'

'Mmm. Is there anything you'd do differently if you had your time over?' His smile was cocky. She'd forgotten what perfect teeth he had. Rita knew exactly what he was getting at and didn't like it.

'No, I don't think so, Frank. I think I've done about as well as I could have done, better than most of the girls I knew, as a matter of fact.'

'It's not too late you know, Rita.'

'For what?'

'You know bloody well what I'm talking about.'

'Don't be stupid. You're drunk.' Rita felt a hot flush coming and searched in her bag for a tissue. 'God, I'm hot.'

'Yeah, maybe so, but I'd lay money that you've wondered what it would have been like, just like I have. And you'll keep wondering.' Sweating now, Rita felt breathless. She tried to light a cigarette, but the wind was picking up, blowing out the flame from her lighter. 'I'm cold, I'm going inside.'

'You just said you were hot.'

'Oh shut up, Frank.' Rita rose and walked a little unsteadily to the ladies'. It was crowded with women re-arranging their hats and touching up their lipsticks. She leaned against the cool porcelain of the basins and looked at her flushed face. She was sweating profusely and her eye make-up was running. She fought an urge to cry and felt angry with herself for drinking so much. She hated the maudlin feeling she got when she'd had too much. She stayed there, just leaning for five minutes until the flush had passed, then splashed her face with cold water, drew herself up straight and combed her hair. As she was coming out she met Douggie and Steve supporting Gully, whose knees were buckling.

'Look at the bloody state of him,' she said.

'We're just going to stick him in a cab love, he's had it.'

'I don't know why you bother taking him anywhere. It's always the same.' Rita looked Gully up and down in disgust and wished Douggie could get himself a best mate who wasn't such a liability.

Back out on the terrace, the rest of the group had returned to their seats. Carefully she avoided Frank and joined Ronnie and Marilyn who were celebrity spotting. 'I'm telling you that's definitely Joan Collins in the Royal Enclosure,' Marilyn was saying to her brother.

'She's little, isn't she? She looks quite a big bird on the telly.' Ronnie squinted into the sunlight.

'Everybody looks bigger on the telly, stupid. Mum, tell him, that's definitely Joan Collins.'

'I can't see properly. Who's got your father's binoculars?' Ronnie handed them to her. 'Oh look Marilyn; there's the Aga Khan talking to the Queen Mother.'

'Who cares about her? She's ancient. Who else can you see?'

'I've just seen Dennis Waterman at the bar, Mum. You like him, don't you?' Ronnie pulled on his mother's sleeve. Rita spun around. *Minder* was her favourite programme, the one thing she and Douggie were in absolute agreement on, and she'd loved Dennis Waterman ever since she saw him on telly in *The Sweeney*. 'Oh, I'd better go and have a look.'

And so passed the remainder of the day. Rita decided that Frank was just pissed and she was better off staying out of his way. She whooped with delight when her horse, Shahrastri won by half a length to become the Derby winner. The odds shortened considerably just before the race, but having taken the SP at the tote, she picked up almost £300, roughly equivalent to the sum Douggie had spent that day on betting and drinks. She didn't want to stay for the remaining races, but Douggie, Steve and Ronnie were trying to make up their losses before they left and it was six o'clock by the time they arrived home through heavy traffic. Rita said there was no way she was cooking that night and offered to buy everybody a takeaway out of her winnings. After the meal Marilyn, Ronnie, Steve and Shelley walked down to the nearest pub in Purley and Douggie and Rita sat on the sofa watching a bit of telly.

She leaned into Douggie and he responded, holding her close to him. After ten minutes he asked if she fancied an early night. There wasn't much on the telly. They went upstairs where they enjoyed some surprisingly good love-making. Rita was surprised to find how much easier it was to fulfil her marital obligations if she imagined she was doing it with somebody else.

CHAPTER NINE

Nice Girls Don't

Marilyn had been juggling her romantic life for a while. At least in her mind she had. On the one hand there was Nelson: reliable, loving, straight as a die, good in bed but boring. She'd met him in a wine bar in South Croydon one Friday evening with her friend Michelle who had said, 'Oh my God, that's Nelson Watts, he's beautiful, Marilyn, he used to go out with Charmaine Pearce, don't you remember?'

They'd been seeing each other on and off for nine months and Marilyn was getting restless. They had quite different ideas about what constituted a good time. Nelson thought drugs were for morons and wouldn't even smoke a joint. All you should really hope for from life, he often said, was work you enjoyed and love. If Marilyn turned up speeding like a dervish he would be really moody and quiet and that pissed her off no end. Why couldn't he just relax? He was only twenty-two. He even said that he believed in God once, but Marilyn had laughed so scornfully that the subject was never raised again. He worked hard at college where he was studying for a degree in electronic engineering and yes, he was good at the love bit – she'd had some cracking evenings in his little flat by West Croydon bus station – but Marilyn wanted excitement. Nelson claimed that the clubs in the West End she rated so highly were full of pseuds and wankers. She didn't know what a pseud was but could tell from his tone that it was some sort of a dig.

He had a lovely family with loads of brothers and sisters who'd made her feel really welcome on the few occasions he'd taken her back to their house on the Pollards Hill estate. But he could never really be her boyfriend properly because he was West Indian – her dad would hit the roof. Actually he was only half West Indian because his mum was white, but just a touch of the tar brush would be enough to set Douggie against him. Marilyn hadn't yet got to the stage where she could defy her father and lose his financial support, which she knew absolutely definitely would be the first thing to go.

Then there was Mark. He wasn't as good-looking as Nelson, but he was older, had plenty of money and an edge. Nothing had happened yet but it was on the cards – she could feel it. When he took her downstairs to the office at the club to give her a line – which he did only for her and not any of the other girls – he would lean in really close and after he'd snorted his eyes would shine and he'd squeeze her arm. Marilyn thought it was hysterical getting wired when her dad was upstairs in the bar and Mark would look at her and wink if Douggie gave her a pat on the back for working hard and having so much energy. Mark had asked her once if she fancied coming back for a drink to his flat in Pimlico after work, but she'd been unable to face making an excuse to Douggie and had returned home as usual with her father in a minicab. Though she did one shift mid-week when Douggie wasn't there, she had college the next morning and didn't want to have to sneak back home in the middle of the night. When she did stay the night with Mark, she wanted to be able to wake up the next day beside him. But three weeks had passed since he'd asked her and Marilyn was worried that perhaps he thought she was just a kid, too scared of what her dad might think, and wouldn't ask her again.

Although she knew deep down that it was bound to happen sooner or later – she kept getting the initial M when she added up the numbers on her bus ticket – there was the dilemma of exactly when to chuck Nelson. She didn't want to get rid of him too soon and be without a boyfriend, but having two boyfriends on the go was unthinkable. Only slags did that. She decided she'd wait until it happened with Mark and then get rid of Nelson. Life would be a lot easier once she started going out with Mark. For starters, Douggie was bound to be pleased – at least Mark was white. Her mum had told her that she wouldn't trust any of the Skinners further than she could throw them, but that was her mum all over, always looking for fault. Funny thing was, Rita would probably prefer Nelson to Mark even though he was the wrong colour. She'd often told her daughter: 'You want to get yourself a nice steady bloke with a good job. You don't want any ponces or anybody too fast and remember, it's just as easy to fall in love with a rich man as it is a poor one.' Mark had a steady job at the club but there was an element of danger and excitement about him that her mum wouldn't have approved of.

When Mark hadn't turned up at the Derby Marilyn had been sorely disappointed. She'd gone and bought herself a new suit especially, cream skirt and jacket with black trim that Douggie had given her the money for on the condition that she didn't tell her mother. The following evening when she turned up for her shift at the club he hadn't been there either and Greg the barman was in charge. He told her that Mark had been in Amsterdam for a couple of days; nobody seemed to know what he did there, but it was a trip he'd made a couple of times in recent months. She'd barely been able to get through her shift, weighed down with disappointment and the lack of coke from Mark.

The following day she went to the covered market in Tooting with Michelle where they bought some shoes and each paid their fiver to see the fortune-teller. Madame Jeanie told Marilyn that there were two men in her life and that only one of them was right. One would bring her misery and the other much happiness. It was enough of a sign for her to decide then and there to chuck Nelson the following evening, Friday, and make her pitch for Mark on the Saturday. With Michelle's encouragement she decided that she would just be bold and ask him if he fancied doing something after work, a pretty unequivocal invitation seeing as they didn't finish until 2 a.m. 'I feel sorry for Nelson though,' said Michelle, 'he's really nice.'

She broke the news in Rumours, the wine bar in South Croydon where they'd met, and Nelson didn't take it very well. Although Marilyn insisted that she hadn't met anybody else, he'd known her long enough to know when she was lying. She kept saying that she thought they weren't getting anywhere, that she wanted her freedom and besides, once she'd left college in a couple of weeks she was probably going to get a job in town and a flat to go with it. This wasn't wholly untrue. She didn't tell him, or anybody else for that matter, that the flat she was planning to make a home in was Mark's in Pimlico. It was taking a lot for granted, but it was only natural when two people were mad about each other the way she and Mark were. She'd had enough of living at home and kept repeating, 'I want to move on, change my life. You don't understand, Nelson, I just don't fit in around here, Croydon's boring.'

'Yeah but all your friends and family are here, you don't know anybody in London.' It was a good point but Nelson was clutching at straws. They sat quietly finishing their bottle of wine until he stood up and said he was going home.

'Can I come with you?' Marilyn asked. The wine had made her feel affectionate.

'What for?'

'Well, you know, I don't want us to part on bad terms.'

'You're fucking mad.' Nelson looked her up and down with a look that hovered somewhere between pity and disgust. 'You're losing it, Marilyn, I don't know how much of that gear you're sticking up your nose, but I think it's shrivelled your brain.'

'Oh piss off then, if that's your attitude.' Marilyn sulkily finished her drink and cigarette and walked out on to the high road to get a bus. She was surprised at how choked she felt.

But by the following morning she had rallied. She'd passed the remainder of Friday evening at home with her mother, an unusually congenial couple of hours spent watching the television, drinking bottles of Guinness and smoking cigarettes. Rita could tell Marilyn had been crying when she came home, but had learned from experience not to ask after her daughter's welfare if she didn't want to be on the end of a mouthful. Rita did what mothers do well – wittered on about the shop, the garden and even got in a few digs at Steve's girlfriend Shelley which pleased Marilyn no end.

As Marilyn sat in her dad's big reclining chair she thought that maybe the odd night indoors wasn't such a bad thing. Rita waited until she was washing up the glasses and getting ready to turn in for the night before asking her, 'Are you still seeing that nice boy, Nelson, isn't it?'

'No. Anyway I wasn't seeing him, he was just a friend.'

'Oh, right.' Rita hovered in the doorway but thought better of pursuing it. 'All right then love, night-night.'

'Night, Mum.'

On Saturday evening Marilyn arrived for her shift early at the Poland with her dad. She'd made a special effort and though there wasn't much flexibility with a uniform of black and white she was wearing tight ski pants and a button-up sleeveless blouse that highlighted her sunbed tan well. Since starting her college course, she had become a devotee of the recently invented electric beach. She wore her hair up with loose wisps trailing down to soften the effect and her make-up was flawless. Even her father commented on how nice she looked. Douggie said he wanted to get in half an hour early and have a word with Frank about the proposed refit for the club. Frank had a friend that was willing to supply them with Italian marble for transport costs only. Something for nothing was not unappealing to Douggie.

While the men talked downstairs, upstairs the bar staff and Mark were preparing for a big night. All the fridges had been emptied the previous evening and had to be completely restocked. There were still a lot of glasses that last night's shift hadn't washed and Marilyn and Eimar were busy polishing while Mark walked around whistling, jangling his big bunch of keys and bringing up bottles of spirits for the barmen. Something had put him in a good mood and he made the unusual gesture of cracking a bottle of champagne and offering each of them a drink before the club opened.

'What's this in aid of?' Marilyn asked.

'We're going to be busy tonight, I just thought it would be nice to have a livener before we started.' Mark winked at Marilyn and brushed his hand against her backside as he moved along the bar.

'I saw that,' Eimar whispered to Marilyn. 'Are you and your man . . . you know?'

'No.' Marilyn was coy. 'Not yet.' Both girls sniggered.

'Well watch yourself. He's sexy all right, but I'd say he's as tricky as hell.'

'He's not seeing anybody, is he?'

'Oh no, not that I know of, but he's not the settling down type is he really?'

'Maybe he just hasn't met the right girl?' Marilyn's face flushed.

'Jesus. Famous last words. How many women have I heard say that about eejits?' She put down her teatowel and pulled her cigarettes out of her bag from behind the bar. 'Come on, let's have a quick ciggie before we open.'

Douggie and Frank emerged from downstairs and started walking around the club discussing where they'd have all the marble that was coming their way. Mark called over to where the two girls were having their cigarettes: 'Marilyn can you come down to the office for a minute? I haven't got your hours for last week, so I can't put your wages through.'

Eimar nudged Marilyn. 'Hours my bloody arse.'

Marilyn rose and, straightening her blouse, tried to walk slowly across the floor of the club. Her heart was banging in her chest as she descended the staircase. She walked into the office to find Mark hunched over the desk. 'Close the door. Come and sit here.'

She sat on the swivel chair next to his and looked curiously at the small brown bottle he was holding up between finger and thumb. 'What's that?'

'A present.' He unscrewed the top, which came away with a small spoon attached to it. He scooped it into the bottle and inhaled the contents noisily up one nostril, then refilled it and offered the same to Marilyn. Though no stranger to the gear she found it shocking to inhale that much at once. While they both sniffed noisily, he screwed the top back on the bottle and handed it to her. 'Here you go, it's all yours. It's getting a bit dodgy coming down here together, with your old man and my old man hanging about.' Marilyn looked in the bottle. There had to be two or three grams inside it, at least.

'I can't take all that, Mark.' She inhaled deeply to try and quieten her racing heart. 'Bloody hell, it's strong.'

'It's hardly been cut at all. It's fucking lovely.' He jumped up and started whistling. 'Don't go too mad on it or you'll have a heart attack.' He looked at her and ran a finger from the side of her face, down her neck and across her collarbone, stopping just above her breast. 'Save some for later.'

Marilyn left the office feeling slightly out of control and anxious that she wouldn't be able to keep it together in front of her dad. She'd never seen a coke bottle before and clutched the brown glass in the palm of her hand feeling very grown up. No more sodding about with her travelcard and a

£5 note on the back of the toilet. She dropped the bottle into her bag behind the bar, pretending to look for a comb. She didn't notice Douggie walk up behind her looking for a pencil by the till. It made her jump when he said, 'All right then Dewdrop, ready to go?'

'Jesus Christ, Dad, don't sneak up on me like that, you scared me to death!'

'What? I was just looking for a pencil. What's the matter with you?'

'Nothing,' Marilyn snapped. 'Just don't creep around like that, it sets my nerves on edge.' Douggie mumbled something about moody women and walked back to Frank. He took the pencil from behind his ear and made little sketches on the back of a betting slip.

Mark came bounding up the stairs two at a time smiling broadly, his eyes blazing. He paused for a short chat with his father and Douggie, made a few enthusiastic comments about the refit, then took up position at the end of the bar where he could keep an eye on the till transactions. Although he made matey conversation with the barmen they resented his ever-watchful behaviour. By nine the club was filling up quickly and there was little time for anything other than suggestive eye contact with Marilyn.

Meanwhile, in the little flat above a car-spares shop in West Croydon, Nelson was thinking. He was sure that Marilyn really did love him and he persuaded himself that the real reason for her calling a halt to their relationship was her father's prejudice. She'd been quite frank with him when he'd wondered after a couple of months why he hadn't met her family, but he never actually thought that it could seriously come between them. He'd met the same thing in varying degrees with other girlfriends but experience had taught him that the parents usually came round once they'd got to know him and bothered to look beneath the skin.

She'd probably been too ashamed to admit the real cause for her decision and now Nelson realised that the onus was on him to do something about it.

Lying around somewhere was a box of matches from the club with the address on. He pulled his suit out of the wardrobe and ironed a shirt. He'd already drunk four cans of beer but thought better of starting on the Scotch if he was going to meet her father. If he could just talk to her dad and explain how he felt about her, he was sure he could make it all right.

While Nelson shaved, rehearsing in his bathroom mirror what he would say to her father, the object of his affections was locked in the ladies' stall at the club with a small spoon jammed under her right nostril. For some reason she couldn't fathom, the left one hadn't worked for weeks. She put it down to a summer cold. She concentrated, to steady her breathing, and let the cleanest cocaine she'd ever experienced take hold. As she was making the appropriate flushing sounds for the benefit of the small group of women patiently assembled outside, the main door of the ladies' swung open and Eimar breathlessly shouted, 'Come on Marilyn, it's going fucking ballistic up there.' Marilyn zipped her coke bottle in the little side pocket of her handbag for safe keeping and came out smiling apologetically to the harassed Eimar. 'Sorry.'

'I thought you'd fallen down the bleedin' toilet. Look, a group of Frank's mates have just come in, I don't like the look of them so you can serve them and I'm going to collect some glasses. Why they don't get a bus boy is anybody's guess.'

The muffled sounds of the club exploded into full volume in her head as Marilyn ascended the small staircase. She felt a bit of a rush, unsure if she could take that much stimulation all at once, but ploughed on regardless. She retied her white apron, chucked her bag behind the bar and just as her father was pointing and about to open his mouth, said loudly, 'I know, I'm just on my way over.'

Marilyn pushed through the crowd to find Frank seated at his favourite table, the large round one in a recess at the back of the club, with Mark and five men she'd never seen before. The table was partly shielded by the piano, where on Saturday nights a glum, grey-haired pianist desultorily played pub tunes. His fading matinée idol looks suggested better times in the entertainment business. Now, down on his luck, he was forced to play the Poland for £100 a night. Marilyn struggled to hear the drinks order against 'Blue Spanish Eyes'. Three of the men in Frank's crowd were about his age and smartly dressed. The two younger ones were a bit older than Mark, thirty maybe, also suited and booted. One of them, a very blond man with white eyebrows and almost invisible lashes, seemed to like the look of Marilyn. As she stood waiting for them to make up their minds, she could feel his eyes unashamedly looking her up and down. She gave him her best dirty look but he laughed at her. After much deliberation, the group decided on pink champagne.

Marilyn worked her way back through the crowd to the bar and asked her father, 'Who are those blokes with Frank, Dad?' Douggie, having mastered some of the basic elements of bartending, was pouring ice into the sinks. Now he was feeling on top of his game he couldn't stay away from the bar. He got stuck in and his willingness to drag up cases of beer from downstairs or even go collecting glasses had earned him respect among the staff.

'Some geezers with a haulage firm in Southampton, Frank said. Why?'

'Nothing. Just wondered. One of them's a bit fresh, that's all.'

'Just keep out of his way, he won't do anything while Frank's there.' Douggie wiped his hands on his apron. 'Anyway, what are they drinking?'

Marilyn barged back through the crowd, her tray heavy with two bottles of champagne and seven glasses. Eimar followed behind with the ice-buckets. When Marilyn poured the champagne and placed full glasses before each of them most just nodded and Mark didn't even look at her. Only the blond – 'Call me Wizzy' – spoke. 'Sorry babe, can you get me a glass of just regular champagne, the pink stuff's too sweet for me.' Marilyn, reluctant to elbow her way through the crowd again, made the kind of face that the most determined punter would quail before.

'Please?'

Marilyn was getting shirty.

'Pretty please.' Wizzy blew her a kiss as she made her way back to the bar.

'Give us a glass of champagne quickly, Greg.' He nodded, pulled an almost empty bottle out of the fridge and just managed to squeeze a glass out of it. Marilyn was bumped and spilled some of the drink, but it wasn't the short measure he objected to:

'It's flat. I hate flat champagne. Get me a fresh one this time, darling. Please.' As he winked at Marilyn and put his glass on her tray his other hand travelled up the inside of her trouser leg, stopping midway up her thigh. Too stunned to speak, Marilyn headed back to the bar where Eimar registered the look on her face.

'What's happened, Marilyn?'

'One of those friends of Frank's just tried to touch me up. And he complained about his champagne being flat.'

'Oh, did he now. Well, we'll see about that won't we, Greg?' Eimar exchanged knowing smiles with the barman. Greg opened a fresh bottle of champagne and took it, with a glass, into the kitchen, followed by Eimar who said to Marilyn, 'Come on, you'll enjoy this.'

'Ladies first.' Greg nodded to Eimar who smiled, cleared her throat and spat into the glass.

'Your turn.' She handed the glass to Marilyn.

'I can't.'

'Why not indeed?' demanded Eimar.

'It's dirty.'

'Did you say your man just tried to get his hand in your knickers?'

'Yeah.'

'Well, go on then.' Marilyn spat timidly into the glass.

'Come on, a big gobful, you can do better than that,' Eimar encouraged her. Marilyn took a deep breath and spat heartily. Greg topped the glass up to the brim with lively, new champagne and mixed it with an unsavoury finger.

'I can't give it to him, he'll know. I'll start laughing.' Marilyn screeched with delighted horror.

'You're not going to give it to him, I am. He won't sod me around, that's for sure.'

Nelson had little trouble persuading the receptionist, Amanda, that he needed to come in to see Marilyn. He seemed such a nice, polite man, if a little anxious. Quite unlike anybody she would have imagined to be a friend of one of the Fishers and certainly not the type the Skinners would be acquainted with.

Nelson worked his way over to the bar, squinting into the darkened crowd for signs of Marilyn. Smoke hung heavy and people were talking loudly enough to be heard over the noise of the piano. A middle-aged man stacking beer bottles in crates looked friendly enough – the cellar man, Nelson thought.

'Excuse me.' Nelson cleared his throat and repeated more loudly against the clatter of empty bottles, 'Erm, excuse me please.' Douggie spun round and wiped his hands on the back of his trousers. He looked the black man up and down. He seemed harmless enough. At least he was smartly dressed.

'Yes son, what can I do for you?'

'Is Marilyn around please?'

'Marilyn?'

'Yes, Marilyn.'

'What, my Marilyn?' Douggie's eyebrows knotted and Nelson gulped.

'Are you Mr Fisher?' Douggie nodded. 'Mr Fisher, I'm Nelson Watts, I spoke to you once on the phone.'

The two men looked at one another steadily. Douggie could see the steely but respectful look in his eyes. Not taking his eyes off Nelson's face, which he scanned fascinated, wondering if his daughter had kissed it, Douggie shouted to Eimar, 'Oi, Paddy whack, where's Marilyn?'

'On the bleedin' missin' list again.'

Eimar quickly sized up the situation. 'I think I probably know where I can find her though. What's your name?' she asked him softly. When Nelson replied, she winked kindly at him. 'I'll just get her for you. I expect you'd like a beer while you're waiting?' she said loudly, more for Douggie's benefit.

'Yeah, thanks.' Eimar disappeared and after a lengthy pause Nelson attempted some awkward conversation. 'Busy, I see. Is it always like this?'

Down in the ladies', Eimar pushed her way through a crowd of preening women at the mirror. Only one stall was occupied and she banged on it loudly. 'Come on you, there's somebody upstairs wants to see you.'

Marilyn tried to sniff quietly. 'Who?' she asked.

'Nelson. Now come on, Marilyn, I'm fed up with working my tits off while you snort yourself stupid down here.'

Marilyn threw the coke bottle carelessly into her bag, not taking the time to zip it into the side pocket. She came flying out of the cubicle.

'Oh God, don't let my dad see him.'

'Too late. He's at the bar talking to him now.'

Marilyn took the stairs two at a time and arrived flushed at the bar. She looked anxiously from man to man.

'Nelson was just telling me that he's up for a job working for the Ministry of Defence. It's a decent living, electronic engineering.'

Douggie seemed relaxed, leaning across the bar. He was a nice kid, Nelson, not his fault he was black. Douggie, like many a blusterer, was easily won round. Sensing his daughter's discomfort he picked up his bucket. 'Right then, I'll let you kids get on with it. I'm off to get some ice.' They both smiled at him, but as soon as he was out of earshot Marilyn hissed:

'What the fuck are you doing here?'

'I wanted to talk to you, but I can see that there's no point while you're like this.'

'Like what?'

'Marilyn, you've got a load of white powder falling out of your right nostril, for Christ's sake. Haven't you got any pride?'

'How dare you! Go on, piss off.' Hastily she cuffed her dripping and powdery nose.

'Yeah, when I've finished my beer.'

Marilyn looked at the bottle still almost full in front of him. He was such a slow drinker. He looked handsome that night, though; he'd obviously made an effort to scrub up and the way he looked at her with that mix of pity and longing made her want to cry. The gear could get you that way, Marilyn decided. Sudden rushes of emotion that disappear as quickly as they come. Nelson turned away from her and casually struck up conversation with the hang-dog pianist who'd just stopped for his break.

Marilyn stomped into the kitchen and burst into tears. Eimar came through with a tray of dirty glasses and looked at her, but offered no sympathy. She couldn't stand druggies — they talked rubbish and were a selfish pain in the arse. Liars, too. Why people couldn't just get pissed was beyond her. There was something pathetic about Marilyn. 'Don't worry, shift's almost finished,' she said before walking out again.

The bar was heaving, the noise level rising as people became more drunk. Even with no pianist it was hard to hear what the person next to you was saying and conversations had to be conducted directly into the side of people's heads. A couple of customers, overcome, had already been led away from the club. Douggie was at the bar talking to a car dealer from the Old Kent Road who said he should give him a ring if he fancied going down to the auctions in Hastings. Reckoned you could pick up some gems if you could be bothered to get down there early enough on a Sunday morning.

'Yeah, I might do that, mate, stock's getting a bit low. I'll take your number just in case. Hold on a minute, you can never find a bloody pen in this place.' Douggie scanned the bar without luck and then saw his daughter's handbag. 'She's bound to have one in here somewhere.' Crouching down behind the bar he pulled the bag off the low shelf and its contents spilt on to the floor. 'Christ all-bloody-mighty, look at the shit these girls keep in their bags.'

He laughed and began piling lipsticks, notebooks and perfume bottles back into the leather bag. His eye fell on the little glass bottle which was rolling across the floor. 'What's this?' He picked it up and looked at it, then unscrewed the top and looked inside. His face became thunderous. Marilyn was walking back to the bar with an order; her heart stopped when she saw what her father was holding. She tried to turn and walk away but Douggie had seen her.

'What the fuck is this?' her father demanded. Marilyn froze. She couldn't speak. As last orders was called and the lights in the bar went up, they stood there looking at one another. Mark walked over and sized up what was going on. He stood behind Douggie and shot her a look of warning. Finally, she stammered, 'It's not mine.' Mark looked at her furiously.

'Well whose is it then?'

Marilyn faltered.

'It's Nelson's.'

'What's it doing in your bag, then?'

'He asked me to hold on to it for him.'

Douggie stamped on the small bottle with his foot, crushing the glass, then marched round the other side of the bar and grabbed Nelson's arm roughly. Marilyn looked aghast at the shattered glass and coke on the dirty, wet floor of the bar. A hush fell over the crowd at the bar.

'Right, you. Out.' Nelson shook his arm free.

'What you talking about?'

'Giving my daughter drugs! You've got some front coming in here.'

'I don't do drugs.' Nelson was calm.

'No, and I bet you haven't got six kids by different women either. You're all the same your bloody lot. Go on, sling your fucking hook, before I lose my temper. And don't come near my daughter again.'

Things deteriorated rapidly. Mark closed in on Douggie and tried to calm him down, which simply made him worse. Frank tried to lead Douggie down the stairs towards the office, but he shook him off roughly. Frank motioned to the doormen to clear the club quickly and get Nelson off the premises before Douggie went for him. Nelson wrestled his arms free from the doormen and explained that he could leave perfectly well on his own, but not before he gave Douggie his parting shot: 'I think you'll find the problem won't go away just because I do, Mr Fisher.'

His cool infuriated Douggie, who lunged and would have struck him, had Mark and Frank not been on hand to hold him back. Someone at the bar shouted, 'Go on, Douggie, hit him!' The remaining punters, dazed with drink, stepped back to make room for the fight. Marilyn stood quietly, shaking. Disgusted with everybody, Douggie grabbed his jacket from the kitchen and went to leave.

'Dad . . .' Marilyn pleaded.

'Get away from me, you. Just wait till I tell your mother.' Douggie left dramatically, knocking over a couple of chairs as he went, leaving the last few stragglers gaping in his wake. Marilyn tried to run after him, but Mark stopped her.

'Leave him, it'll be all right. Just let him cool off.'

Marilyn stared dejectedly down the street at her father's angry figure striding away through the night-time crowd towards Oxford Street.

'Don't worry, I'll talk to him.' Frank coolly checked his pockets for keys and money. 'And I want to talk to you too in the morning,' he said to his son, before heading off down the street after Douggie.

As their cab sped through the night to Pimlico, Mark put a reassuring arm around Marilyn. Though she still felt sick with anxiety, Mark had more or less convinced her that she'd handled the situation as best she could. She'd done the right thing blaming Nelson, he told her.

'Who was that geezer anyway?'

'Old boyfriend.'

'Want a new one?'

Mark's confidence was infectious. Marilyn laughed and leaned into him.

'Listen, everything's going to be all right. My old man will find him. They'll go back to the club and be up drinking all night. Your dad will go home and sleep it off and by tomorrow night it will all have blown over.'

'Yeah, I suppose so.'

'In the meantime,' he nibbled at her neck, 'just forget about it and enjoy yourself.'

'Oh yeah. How am I going to do that?' Marilyn teased.

Mark slipped his hand under her blouse and kissed her firmly. 'Bit of this, bit of that.' They held each other in the taxi just as their parents had done almost sixteen years ago. 'And there's plenty more snort indoors, so don't worry about that either.'

They climbed the steps to Mark's second-floor flat and Marilyn was surprised to hear late-night television coming from inside. She tugged Mark's sleeve anxiously.

'Don't worry, it's just a mate I've got staying for a couple of days, he won't bother us.' Marilyn was put out to find the blond man from the club sprawled on the sofa, watching a violent film. The sound of gunfire echoed loudly in the large room.

The flat was big but furnished only with essentials, lacking the little touches that might have made it feel homely. Marilyn gazed at the carpet that obviously hadn't seen a hoover for months. The sofa and chair were of black leather and chrome and a set of weights sat underneath the window. It was a classic bachelor set-up. On the glass coffee table were the smears and streaks of cocaine use.

The blond man nodded briefly and Mark introduced them: 'Marilyn this is Wizzy, he was with us earlier.'

'Oh, hello.' Marilyn felt a bit sick.

'Come on.' Mark led her into the bedroom. It was pretty bare, painted dark blue, with a bed and chest of drawers. Clothes were thrown over the back of a typist's chair. Mark went to the kitchen and fetched a bottle of champagne and two glasses. Marilyn said she was a bit worried about the man in the front room.

'Oh, he's all right, he won't bother us. He can't hear, don't worry.'

Marilyn had never made love on cocaine and was thrilled with the new sensations. Everything seemed heightened and she felt a confidence she'd never experienced in bed with a man before. She surprised herself by encouraging him verbally, pulling him down towards her, more bold than she'd ever dared to be. She just knew it would be great with Mark.

He was a bit rough, but she found to her surprise that she quite liked it. Nelson had been so tender, it made a nice change.

What she hadn't bargained for was how impossible it was for both parties to climax on the gear. After Mark had been penetrating her fairly roughly for almost an hour, Marilyn was growing tired and sore. He'd stopped kissing and fondling her too, and was just insistently pushing into her.

'Mark, can we stop for a minute,' she whispered. He rolled off brusquely and without looking at her, chopped more lines on the bedside table. She was growing uneasy, but sniffed heartily and felt the powder start to work its magic again. He climbed back on top and looked at her strangely.

'Getting bored?'

'No, honestly. I was just a bit dry, that's all.'

'We'd better spice it up a bit for you then.' He reared up and called loudly, 'Wiz, Wiz! Come on, mate!'

'What are you doing?' A wave of panic shot through her. He ignored her and called out again. The blond man appeared at the bedside.

'Stop it, Mark! Stop it! Get him out of here.' But Mark continued to push into her with increasing brutality.

'Go on, mate, go on, stick it in her mouth!' Mark cried.

'Oh my God, please don't—'

'Go on, mate, she loves it.' Marilyn could see the two faces above her: both appeared to be sneering. The blond man stood watching, fully clothed, making no move. Marilyn began to sob. 'Please get off, stop it.' Finally the blond man spoke. 'Nah, leave it, mate, she's a fucking kid, she can't handle it.'

He leaned down and roughly grabbed Marilyn's wet face. 'Shouldn't play with the big boys if you can't hack it, you little slag.' She cried out in anguish. He laughed contemptuously and left the room. Mark rolled off her impatiently and Marilyn turned on to her side where she curled up into a ball, crying.

'Oh stop crying, you stupid little cow.' He chopped himself another line, snorted it then walked to the bottom of the bed where her clothes lay in a heap. 'Get dressed,' he ordered. Fishing, his trouser pocket he pulled out a couple of twenties, which he dropped on top of her crying form.

'Go on, get dressed and then get yourself a cab.'

Five minutes later, Marilyn tiptoed past the two men in the front room, who completely ignored her. She ran down the steps out into the street to look for a cab. Shivering in the early morning light with tears streaming down her face, she mumbled to herself:

'Oh, Dad, Dad, I'm sorry, Dad.'

CHAPTER TEN

If Loving You Is Wrong . . .

Rita was feeling the lassitude of summer. She loved her twice-weekly trips to Covent Garden in the bright early dawn but business was slow. It was a seasonal thing; mid-July when the kids broke up from school, men were forced to spend time with their families and the money that would usually go on bouquets for their mistresses was spent on lollies and ice-creams, fruit machines, Wimpy dinners and the constant drain of 'Not another 50p, I gave you your pocket money this morning.' In her flower shop during the slow hours of summer 1986, Rita passed the time considering the business of extramarital love. It was as if she only dared think about it in the shop. To daydream in the home she had made with Douggie was wrong.

To divert herself, she toyed with the idea of a few improvements in the shop. Glass-fronted cold cabinets would keep the flowers fresh for longer – it was criminal the amount of flowers that just wilted and died in the heat, especially the roses. Although a long outdoor roller-blind bearing the name RITA'S shielded the shop from the worst of the heat, a lone fan creaking slowly round did little to move the air and she was wondering how much air conditioning would cost on top. She'd saved £1,400 with the extra bits Douggie gave her from the club and although she had £6,000 in the building society, it was secret money she was loath to touch. 'Bolt money, that's what you need, love,' her mum used to tell her. 'That way when they play up, you've always got that little bit they don't know about and you can either bugger off yourself or tell them to sling their hook.'

Rita decided on getting an estimate and then applying for a business loan from the bank. She wouldn't tell Douggie; she was beginning to realise she only consulted him on business matters to stroke his ego and couldn't be bothered to do it any more. It wasn't as if she didn't understand perfectly well how to run her shop. If she told him of her plans, he would absolutely forbid her to take a loan out because of the interest. He'd find a mate to do the work, pay for everything in cash and declare nothing. Oh, he was generous all right, but Rita thought it might be quite nice to look at her bank statement and instead of seeing deposit figures that bore little relation to the truth, be able to moan about the amount they were charging her for the loan like a respectable shopkeeper. She once floated the notion of registering for VAT but Douggie swore blind it was the ruin of many an enterprising business. 'I've known people just ticking over and doing all right for years, then they register for the VAT and before you know it those bastards are investigating you. They find one luncheon voucher that can't be accounted for and they close you down. Forget it, Rita.'

Since Derby Day Rita had undergone a subtle change of mood and was given to daydreaming. Frank had set her thinking. For as long as she could remember, she had taken her marriage for granted. The longer she'd been married, the less she gave it any thought. But now she dared to wonder what, if anything, they still had between them and hadn't come up with much beyond a mutual love for their children. The love you felt for your kids, Rita concluded, was an arbitrary affair and each had their favourites, but between them she and Douggie just about had the three covered. Since Steve had left home the house had been divided in two with Rita and Ronnie in allegiance and Marilyn and her dad as thick as thieves. But there too the balance was shifting. Douggie had to face the fact that his little girl was no angel, and he didn't like it.

Despite Frank's best efforts to mollify him with a couple more drinks, Douggie had come home ranting and raving in the early hours of Sunday morning, saying that was the end of it. Marilyn could pack her bags if that's how she wanted to live. A totally vindicated Rita had found herself in the unusual position of sticking up for Marilyn as well as Nelson, whom she'd never met. He didn't sound the type. 'Didn't I just know that something like this was going to happen? There's more chance that somebody in *your* club gave it to her than some kid from Croydon College, Douggie.'

Marilyn had arrived home about two hours after her dad that Sunday, looking very wobbly. Though practised in turning on the waterworks if she thought it would get her out of the shit, she was now showing genuine contrition. She confessed that it hadn't been Nelson's coke, but yes, somebody had given it to her at the club. She wouldn't say who. She said she didn't want to go back there to work, which at least saved Douggie the bother of sacking her. Rita had always known her husband wasn't brain of Britain, but she was beginning to dislike what she saw as stupidity. Something like this had been on the cards since the beginning. Douggie might have been street-smart twenty years ago, but it was a totally different world then and he'd since grown up into an overfed suburban car dealer. His days of fancying himself as hard were behind him. When he admitted to his wife in bed that night, 'It's out of my league, Reet', she cringed for him.

Ronnie enjoyed the row and only kept his head down for a few days before saying he wouldn't mind taking over Marilyn's old job for the summer. The next morning, Rita went to the building society, drew out some of her emergency fund and packed him off to Spain to join Spencer and his parents. There was a while to wait before the results of his exams and she wasn't having him working in the club. Although Ronnie wasn't really old enough, Douggie would have preferred it to his being idle for the whole summer. 'Kids need to work so they can learn the value of money, Rita.' She could brain Douggie sometimes.

Leaving Douggie was unthinkable because it would upset the kids too much. But she had started indulging in fantasies of his death. Nothing nasty, mind, just a heart attack or something equally quick. Maybe he could get run over. Then she could do what she liked, see who she liked. Rita wondered if lots of women of her age had widow fantasies; it would make sense if they did – nobody likes to be a home-wrecker. She told herself that she had few illusions about Frank Skinner, but thought about him a lot all the same.

Frank had the edge on Douggie in all the obvious ways. Physically he was fit, had a full head of hair and a hard, handsome face. He'd always worn good threads and was never short of a roll of cash. For fifty-one, he wasn't an unattractive package. Douggie, on the other hand, was going soft with age and the waist was almost equal to the shoulders in diameter, the hair had fallen out and been washed down the plughole. Apart from his suits for work, his wardrobe was left entirely to Rita, who out of boredom and resentment rarely cast her net wider than the menswear department in Marks & Spencer. If you'd never seen Frank before in your life you wouldn't quite be able to say where he was from. He looked a bit Italian, maybe Spanish or slightly rich American. Douggie had Croydon stamped through him like a stick of rock. Rita knew it was wrong to compare them, but couldn't help herself.

The last Wednesday in July, she was leaning on the counter in her shop, a pencil between her teeth, looking at that evening's television in her paper. She wished Douggie would make life more interesting by taking the trouble to give her the odd surprise – bring a couple of tickets to Spain home from work or even just the odd weekend away. Since he'd put money in the club they'd neglected the friends with whom they'd regularly socialised. Rita put the pencil behind her ear and rummaged on the shelves under the till for a *Croydon Advertiser* – she would take herself off to the pictures, that would cheer her up. 'Bored, bored, bored, bored, bored,' she was repeating to herself in a loud voice the way Marilyn used to.

'We'll have to do something about that then, won't we?' His familiar voice came from the doorway. Rita shot up.

'Hello Frank, what are you doing in Croydon?' She flushed. Smoothing her hair she added, 'Wouldn't have thought there was much for you around here.'

'I was just on my way back into town from Gatwick. I've got a driver and I have to pay him a full day whatever time I finish with him. I thought I might take you out for lunch, find a pub in the country somewhere. If you fancy it.'

Frank was looking tanned and very relaxed with his pale blue shirtsleeves rolled up and wearing a pair of navy linen trousers. Rita looked down at her knee-length shorts beneath her pinny and T-shirt.

'I can't go like this.'

'Well, you're closing in a minute, aren't you, it's Wednesday, half-day. We can take you home to get changed if you like.' Rita thought of Flossie doing the ironing back at the house and what she'd say if she saw Rita with Frank. If she saw Frank at all, come to that.

'Oh sod it, I'll go like this as long as you don't mind.'

'Great.' A lazy smile spread across his tanned face. Those teeth.

In the back of the shop, Rita made what repairs she could with a bit of lipstick and a comb. She felt hot and wished there was some scent in her bag. Oh well, never mind: at least she'd shaved her legs the night before. She thought about calling home to tell Flossie that she was going shopping and wouldn't be back till later, then decided against it. Why should she have to explain her movements to Doug's aunt?

After setting the alarm and closing up the shop, Rita stepped out into brilliant sunshine on Selsdon Road where Frank's stretch Mercedes was waiting. She could sense Mrs Singh watching from the sweet shop next door and felt momentarily self-conscious. But inside Rita Fisher a new boldness was growing and there were a few slogans she wanted to shout to the world:

'So what? Have a good look. It's none of your business. Sod you.' She swung into the limousine with a flourish and flashed the smile of a younger woman to the driver as he closed the door for her.

Paperwork was strewn across the floor of the back of the limousine; Frank gathered it and placed it inside his case. She toyed with the idea that he'd put it there for show, just to let her know how important he was, and smiled to herself as the car pulled away from the kerb and the driver asked, 'Where to?'

'What do you fancy then, Reet?'

'Well, there's a nice pub in Warlingham where we can get a good ploughman's or something.'

'Or we can go a bit further afield, nip down to Brighton if you like, it's not far.' Frank stretched one arm up over the top of the seat, behind Rita's shoulders, but not touching. The thought of Brighton panicked Rita, it was so far away. Seeing her face, Frank laughed kindly, implying that there was nothing in the world to worry about. 'If it makes you feel better, then we'll go to Warlingham.' Rita felt silly.

'No, it's OK, let's go to Brighton then.'

'Sure?'

'Yeah. Definitely.' Rita looked out of the windows as the car sped along the A23, away from Croydon, through Purley and on to the Brighton Road past the old Tiffany's, now Cinderella Rockefella's dance hall where Rita had whiled away many a Saturday night in her younger days. She nudged Frank: 'Do you remember that place?' Frank looked out of the window of the car and laughed.

'Do I? Bloody hell it must be over twenty years. No, tell a lie, didn't me and you go once when Douggie was away?' Rita would rather not have been reminded of that episode in their lives.

'Yeah, I think we did.' Frank looked at her strangely and shuffled his papers.

'Look, Rita, I must just finish writing up the notes of this meeting before I forget, do you mind?' Rita peered absent-mindedly at the sheaf of papers.

'No, not at all. Where have you just come from?'

'Spain. I do a bit of business with an old mate from the Elephant who lives in Puerto Banus now.'

'What sort of business?'

'This and that.'

The car sped on and once they'd got through Coulsdon and hit the M23 it took only half an hour until they were on the outskirts of Brighton. The air conditioning was so powerful that Rita's arms and legs were covered in goosepimples. The car phone had rung a couple of times, but each caller had been dispatched with 'Not now, I'm busy.'

Frank snapped shut his briefcase and stretched and yawned. He grabbed Rita's knee but in a friendly way and asked, 'Do you like seafood?'

'Yeah I love it. Winkles, cockles, jellied eels, prawns.'

'Ever been to English's?'

'No, what's that?'

'Really good seafood place, you can get anything you want there, you'll like it.' He checked his watch. 'We'll be fine, it's only quarter to two, I'm sure they serve lunch till about three.'

When the driver had negotiated the limo through Brighton's winding lanes he opened the door for Rita, drawing atten-tion to the stretch Mercedes from which the lady in the

Bermuda shorts and a smart-looking gentleman emerged to the amusement of the other diners in the outside seating area. Inside, Rita noted the traditional décor and the waiters in their starched white shirts and aprons. The other diners were mostly business people dressed in suits who spoke in hushed tones.

'Oh, God, I should have got changed. You didn't say it was like this.' Rita noticed that one other woman was wearing shorts, but she was about sixty and looked American. It didn't count.

'Rita, you look fine, don't worry about it.' Frank's voice was calm. 'Anyway, fuck 'em if they can't take a joke.' He ordered champagne and studied the menu briefly but seemed to know what he wanted before he looked. When the waitress appeared to take their order, he asked, 'Rita, what would you like?'

'I'll have the king prawns please.'

'Are you sure you don't want the lobster?' Frank offered.

'No, just the prawns, thank you.'

'And I'll have a dozen oysters please, love.' He snapped shut the menu and handed it to the waitress. Rita blanched. It was a bit forward of him to order oysters. She could still vividly remember the time Douggie ordered them in that fish restaurant in the West End. She had watched, her face burning with shame and embarrassment, as he'd sucked and slurped the viscous little bits of wobbly fish off the shell, making the mistake of trying to chew them, his face making dissatisfied shapes while all around other diners looked on. It had made her feel quite sick and put her off her breaded plaice.

But when Frank's oysters arrived, he slid a little knife under them to loosen them from the shell and they just slipped down his throat in one swallow. He ate quickly and quietly, no slurping, taking small sips of champagne between mouthfuls. Rita was fascinated watching him, so little conversation passed during the lunch. When he finished eating, Frank carefully wiped the corners of his mouth. Rita tried to stop the comparison but had a vivid image of her husband drawing the back of his hand across his greasy post-dinner face and then wiping the excess on his trousers. She put down her knife and fork. It was then that their silence became uncomfortable. Frank spoke first.

'Look, Rita, about what I said to you the other week. I'm really sorry if I put you on the spot and I shouldn't have said some of the things I did; I don't mean to and then I see you and I end up blurting out all sorts of things.' Rita was flattered but worried that he might be trying to take back his words.

'It's OK. You just took me by surprise, that's all.' Rita shyly smiled down at her empty plate. Frank reached over and squeezed her left hand. She expected him to take it away, but it rested there, holding hers and turning the ring on the third finger. She wished he wouldn't do that. It was probably done absent-mindedly, Rita told herself, but it felt so significant. Frank shook his head and looked away.

'I don't know what to say to you, Rita, I never do. You always get me like this. I feel like a kid after his first snog when I'm around you.'

'That's only because you never got what you wanted the first time,' Rita replied. The thought came out of nowhere and was said before she'd had time to consider its meaning. Frank was taken aback.

'Well, yeah, I suppose there is a feeling of unfinished business. But it's not just that, Rita, it can't be. Not after all these years. I spent so fucking long pretending I wasn't bothered whether or not you loved me. I used to slag you off to myself and say that I didn't like your hair or you were a bit heavy . . .' Rita sat up with a start. 'Not that you were or are, I mean, I just used to say it to myself. Then you married Douggie. I'm such an idiot, Rita.'

'No you're not.'

'You don't know me, not really. I've done a lot of stupid things.' This had the desired effect of piquing her interest and making her want to know him again.

'Like what?'

'The business with Barry Gill you know about. There have been a few other things, but I regret that mostly. That's what really turned you against me.'

'Did his family ever find out what had happened to him?' Rita was direct. Frank bowed his head.

'No.' He heard her sigh. 'Look, Rita, I was young, I panicked. I know that being sorry doesn't bring him back, but confessing wouldn't have helped anybody. Then it would have been two families without fathers, and at least this way I've been able to take care of Doreen and my two kids and Barry's wife and their three.'

'Mmm, you're good at that.' Rita immediately regretted her sarcasm. 'Sorry, I didn't mean to say that.'

'Why not. You've got every right.' Frank drained the bottle into their glasses and waved the empty at the waitress for a refill.

'Have you ever hurt anybody else?' She had to know.

'I didn't mean to hurt Barry, Rita, you know I didn't.'

'I'm not talking about him. Did you hurt anybody else?'

'I've had the odd punch-up, but that's usually to do with drink, so no, I can put my hand on my heart and swear to God that I haven't hurt anybody else.' Frank raised his right hand as he said it. Not being much of a believer, he didn't worry too much about that kind of thing.

'It was very violent back then, wasn't it? I just remember loads of fights with knives and people with scars,' Rita said.

'Mmm.' Frank swilled the champagne in his glass. 'Come on holiday with me, Rita.'

'Oh yeah and say what to Douggie and the kids?' Even if it was implausible, the idea excited her.

'Can't you say you're going with your sister?'

'Mavis? You're joking. She hasn't left Camberwell in fifteen years. Besides, Douggie knows she hasn't got any money and I certainly wouldn't pay for her. I love my sister, but she is one diabolical ponce.'

'Well haven't you got any other mates?' Rita reflected sadly that she didn't have, really. Oh, there were other couples they were matey with, but no women she was really close to, not like years ago when she had Dolly.

'Do you remember my mate Dolly at the Angel?'

Frank laughed. 'Bloody hell, do I! She used to give me a right roasting when I went to drop your money off on a Monday. She'd put a Scotch in front of me, on the house mind, and say, "Drink that and then fuck off, you useless piece of shit." I think it must have been that red hair of hers that made her like that. What's she up to these days, do you still see her?'

'Not for donkey's years. They got a pub down in Margate after the Angel. Me and Doug went a couple of times. You know, days out at the coast with the kids. But it's so far away that we sort of lost touch.'

'Can't you say you're going to see her for a week or something?'

'I don't even know if she's still in Margate. Still, it would be lovely to see her.'

'I wasn't suggesting you really went, just use her name.'

'Douggie would think it was pretty bloody funny, for me just to close the shop up and sod off for a few days to visit a mate I haven't seen in years.'

'What's her second name?' Frank pulled out a pen from his jacket, which was resting on the back of his chair, and clicked the top.

'Furness, Dolly and Bill Furness. I think the pub was called the Fiddler's Arms or the Fiddler's Rest or something like that. Fiddler's something.' Rita searched her memory while

Frank scribbled on the tissue tablecloth which he tore and folded, placing the paper in his top pocket.

'What are you going to do?'

'I'll see if I can track her down. It'll do you good to see some old mates, Rita, you work too hard. You run that shop, that house, look after Doug and those kids.'

Unaccustomed to appreciation, Rita felt heady. Frank added, 'Doreen would have a fit if she had to load her own dishwasher, lazy cow.'

'Don't be rotten. Anyway, if we do go away, what will you tell her?'

'Nothing. I'm always going away on business. Anyway, we lead separate lives.' Frank looked at his watch. 'Right then, we'd better get back. It's four now, we won't get you home till five at the earliest.'

'Yeah, we'd better go.' After paying, they stepped outside and Rita looked up at the blue sky, dotted with white clouds. She could smell the salt in the air and breathed deeply. 'Shame we can't go for a walk along the front, though. It's such a lovely day.'

'Another time eh?' Frank put his hand gently in the small of her back and led her to the car.

Unused to drinking during the day, Rita felt sleepy and a bit miserable on the journey back to Croydon.

'No point mentioning anything to Doug, eh?' Frank suggested.

'Don't be stupid.' Her mood had dipped from its zenith at around the third glass of champagne. Now she just felt grubby being in the back of a limousine with Frank. Nothing had happened, nothing to be ashamed of, except perhaps for her intentions and the keen disappointment she felt that their day had to end. 'Don't drop me right outside the house. Leave me at the bottom of Foxley Lane and I'll walk up.'

'I want to see you again, Rita, properly.' He didn't look at her when he said it, but he squeezed her hand. She gulped.

'So do I, but it's complicated. You're Douggie's partner and we're getting too old for all this carry-on.' She was crushed that he didn't take issue with her.

'Maybe. But look, think about it. I'll be in touch, yeah?' Rita listened to the clicking of the indicators like a death rattle as the car pulled into the kerb. Her day was over and she didn't want to get out of the car. She took her time, checking in her bag to see that she had her keys, cigarettes and purse.

'Thanks a lot Frank, it was lovely. Really it was.' He pulled her into a long embrace and kissed her warmly. It was a luxurious, lazy kiss that left her a bit breathless. As she got out of the car Frank's face seemed stricken by a very real sadness. She climbed the hill along Foxley Lane and watched his head in the back of the car disappear in the distance. He didn't look back.

Rita closed her front door behind her and leaned against it, pleased to be home. She was startled by the rattling of cups from the kitchen. Flossie appeared in the doorway from the kitchen to the front hall, a teatowel collecting drips from her gnarled hands, a cigarette trembling angrily between old lips.

'Flossie, what are you still doing here?'

'Waiting for you, I was worried sick. Where the bloody hell have you been? You're normally back by quarter to one.' Rita walked past her into the kitchen where a huge pile of ironed shirts stared at her reproachfully from the table.

'Oh, Flossie, thanks a lot. Look,' she fumbled in her bag, 'here's your money. You needn't have waited, I'd have dropped it over later.'

'How could I go home, when I was worried about you? You didn't say a word about going out last week. What was I supposed to think?' Flossie coughed, an exercise which took her several minutes to recover from. 'I called Douggie, but he didn't know where you were.'

'What did you do that for?' Rita spun round angrily.

'I was worried. Anyway, you still haven't told me where you were.'

'I went shopping, all right?'

'Well you didn't buy much, where are your bags?'

'What *is* this, the bloody third degree? I'm the only one in this house who isn't allowed to have a life. They all come and go as they please and I can't even spend an afternoon looking round the shops without everybody doing their nut. I'm sick of it.' Rita filled the kettle and angrily banged it down on the counter.

'You want to get down the doctor's, you do.' Flossie's face was pinched as she buttoned up her blue raincoat to the neck.

'What's wrong with me now?' Rita demanded.

'Flying off the handle like that. You're not right, Rita.'

'Oh for crying out loud!' She stomped up the stairs and threw herself on her bed where she surrendered to sobs of frustration and hopelessness. Is this what her life amounted to, being answerable to the woman who came to iron the shirts? She heard the front door bang and went and stood by the window watching Flossie secure a headscarf under her chin as she walked down the hill to the bus stop. She must be bloody boiling, thought Rita, sweating in her shorts and T-shirt. Still, in twenty years' time she would look exactly the same. She'd probably be ironing shirts herself for a bit of pocket money too.

She thought of how quickly that last twenty years had gone and decided that she had to make an effort to enjoy her life now while she still had time. She didn't want to look back to see only duty and routine. She'd forgotten what really enjoying herself was. She picked up the picture of the family on her bedside table and wiped the dusty glass. They didn't need her any more. She had to get a life of her own. She flopped backwards on her giant bed and prayed for change and excitement.

CHAPTER ELEVEN

Bad Juju

Douggie Fisher enjoyed a more or less permanent contentment. His thick skin did him proud and bad feelings could be shrugged off. If he had money worries his sleep could suffer, but he refused to be dogged by vague pessimism. The row with Marilyn took about a week to blow over. Content that she'd learned her lesson, Douggie wasn't going to dwell on ifs and maybes. Neither was he about to give in to his sense of unease. To him hunches were women's business and he had often scorned Rita, who could feel a sideways look through a concrete wall, for her superstitious, omen-seeking nature. 'I believe it if I can see it in front of me,' was Douggie's philosophy.

He radiated relaxation – the permanent smile, generosity with money and unfailing patience. His temper was only bluff and he was easily won round. If somebody told him something, he took them at their word until it was proved otherwise. Douggie had done well to get out of crime when he did. When Frank said that importing buckshee marble for a refit at the club was a harmless affair, Douggie had no reason not to believe him. It was easy, Frank explained. A mate of his with a chemical haulage company would move the marble from Belgium to Southampton. Upon their arrival, the pallets would be transported to the haulage firm's head office on an industrial estate in Andover, from where Douggie would collect them and take them to the club. The marble would be stored in the basement and the builders would come there to cut and fit it. It would take about three or four trips to complete the load but Frank estimated that, allowing for transport costs, they would save in the region of £18,000. As this was almost the size of his stake in the club, Douggie agreed readily to the plan. It was with a happy heart that he drove down the M3 on a bright morning in July with Steven to collect the first consignment of free materials for the redecoration of his club.

The roads out of London were clear and Douggie was enjoying flying along at eighty-five miles an hour in his borrowed lorry while the traffic coming into town had ground to a halt. The thick trees alongside the motorway were drenched in golden light and a fresh breeze blew through his open window. On the radio, Terry Wogan was making him chuckle. Douggie was feeling good. Steven, less so.

'Don't you think it's a bit weird, Dad, getting marble all the way from Belgium via Spain when there must be plenty of it knocking about in London?' Steven pulled one of Shelley's long blonde hairs from his Gabicci sweater as he spoke.

'Nah, not really. Frank does loads of business with this geezer in Southampton who does a lot of haulage for him. Even though the bloke does mostly chemicals, as a favour he'll bring in other stuff for mates. You see, he can get loads of it in because when you import chemicals you pay for the cubic capacity, not the weight.'

'That don't sound right.' Steve straightened the blonde hair between his fingers, admiring its length.

'It's what Frank said.'

'Mmm. Do we have to listen to Radio 2?' Wogan was mimicking a scene from the previous night's episode of *Coronation Street*, his voice working itself into a frenzy.

'Yeah, I like old Terry, he's funny.' Douggie reached into a grease-stained paper bag for his second sausage roll of the journey. Steve turned the volume down. 'Oi! I was listening to that.'

'Yeah, but marble, Dad, think about it. Weighs a fucking ton and it's not like you can't get it anywhere else.'

'Can't get it anywhere else for free.'

'Suppose so.'

Steven traced patterns in the window with his finger. 'Are you sure marble's right for the club though, Dad? I mean, it's all right for a villa in Spain, but a nightclub in Soho?'

'Bloody hell, you're a right wet blanket this morning, what's the matter with you?'

'Nothing.'

'Well shut up then. Where else are we going to get a new bar and tables for nothing?' Flaky pastry crumbs spluttered from Douggie's mouth as he spoke. 'Besides, marble's classy, it'll look terrific.' The two men fell quiet in the front of the van, a comfortable lull interrupted only by Douggie's occasional guffawing at the wit of Wogan. Steven was thinking hard.

'So, what, they bring the marble in on pallets or something?'

'Yeah, of course. How else do you store marble?'

'But wouldn't they store chemicals in drums, Dad?'

'How would I know?'

'Well, didn't Frank tell you?'

Douggie thought his son must be a bit thick.

'Look, all he said was just go to the industrial estate in Andover and ask to see Tom at UK-Chem, Unit 17. We sign for the stuff, load it up and take it back to the club and store it in the basement. Then the builders come in and cut it. Easy.'

'Yeah, but why us? Frank must have a load of lackeys he could get to pick it up.'

Douggie was growing impatient. 'Maybe, Steven, he doesn't trust anybody else. It's thousands of pounds' worth of stuff, anyone could make off with it. Besides, he's out of the country at the moment, he wants to make sure there's no cock-ups, that's why he asked me.'

Steve considered this last statement carefully.

In Sonning another father and son were having a difference of opinion.

Frank Skinner was sitting in his panelled office at home, staring out on to the gardens. Beyond the manicured topiary, great borders of day lilies led to the rose garden in the middle of which a fountain cherub was spouting water.

Mark sat opposite Frank, cleaning his fingernails with a letter-opener. He noted his father's worried expression: 'It'll be all right, Dad, all he's got to do is pick the gear up and store it in the basement. You told him to leave the rest to the builders and not open anything, right?'

'I don't know. I'm beginning to think I've dropped a bollock on this one. I forgot what a bloody liability he is. Can't keep his mouth shut, never could.'

'Well so what? Bragging about a bit of knocked-off marble won't hurt.'

'Yeah, but if Collins gets even a whiff of somebody talking about the run, it'll get ugly.'

'Don't lose your bottle, Dad.'

'You're going to have to learn that there's more to it than bottle. You've got to use this sometimes as well.' Frank tapped the side of his head, then stood up and shoved his hands into his trouser pockets. He rocked back and forth, turned and perched on the edge of his mahogany desk where he punched out some numbers on the hands-free phone. The phone rang for ages and Frank was about to try redial when it was picked up. Frank snatched the receiver:

'Yeah Tom, it's me. What's happening?'

Mark watched his father nodding and uttering, 'Yeah, yeah, OK. Good.' He put the phone down.

'Everything all right?' asked Mark.

'They've just left. Douggie signed for the pallets and

loaded up about quarter of an hour ago. You, get down that club and make sure he doesn't start poking around. Knowing him, he'll want to open up the stuff and have a look.'

'Oh Dad, come on, I thought we were supposed to play golf later? I don't want to go back to town, not in this weather. It's boiling. Anyway, he'll be all right.'

'I said go.'

Frank Skinner paced around his office looking at his symbols of wealth. The least expensive item, his library of first editions, had cost him £12,000 and he'd yet to read a single volume. Tiffany lamps were scattered around the room on desks and occasional tables. The leather chesterfield was rarely sat on and he was plagued by the doubt that maybe greed had got the better of him. He wanted for nothing and wondered if happiness might have been possible with less. If he stopped work tomorrow, he would be comfortable for the rest of his life. He thought of Rita and what she would do if she knew how he was using her husband. Rita might be tired of Douggie but she was loyal to a fault. Having arranged affairs so meticulously, the police would have a hard job tracing anything back to him. But one slip-up and everything could be ruined. Rita would know and it would put paid to any chance he might have of spending time with her. He often tried to regard Rita coldly, see her for the ordinary middle-aged woman that she was, but ordinary or not, she was the one that got away. Frank hated anything that slipped from his grasp. He was so out of sorts that he even craved the company of his wife, but she was upstairs doing what she did every day: sleeping.

Doreen Fisher had long ago found that the most effective way to cope with a loveless marriage was to sleep through as much of it as possible. Pharmaceutical help from the nice doctor on Foxley Lane made this possible. No matter how much money she had to splash around with the other wives of wealthy men in Berkshire, she was never one of them. Oh, they were polite to her, but she was a parvenu and the looks they exchanged when Doreen attempted to join in the conversation never let her forget it. They might have decorators, domestic staff and even art dealers in common, but they were not her friends. Old mates had fallen by the wayside as her lifestyle changed but no new ones had rushed in to fill the void. It was a good job that Mr and Mrs Skinner had a house big enough to accommodate all their unhappiness.

Frank lit a cigar and, ignoring specific instructions not to make contact, dialled the call he'd been building himself up to all morning. He didn't expect to be put through so quickly and was caught off guard when a voice said, 'Make it quick, Frank, I'm in the middle of something.'

Frank faltered for a few seconds then blurted out, 'I'm going to have to back out. I can't do it.'

'How come?' said the voice at the other end of the line coldly.

'I've got a weak link in the chain.'

'Replace it.'

'I can't. I've studied all the options and this is the only one that makes sense. I'm just trying to protect everybody.' Frank's chest thumped with unaccustomed fear.

'This is sad news, Frank, very sad. We spent a long time negotiating to get to here. There were a lot of people who put in tenders for this work, people I've worked with before and trust. You put a lot of effort into persuading me to give you the business and now you've wasted my time. I hate people wasting my time.'

Frank breathed deeply. 'I'd rather call it off than watch it go bandy, that's all.'

'Well we can't stop the second shipment now, it sails in two days' time. It's already left Spain for Belgium, so you'll have to see that one through. Naturally, I'll need the money earlier than we originally agreed and of course there will be penalty fees for cancellation. I'll expect the cash no later than next Saturday. I can't talk now, but I'll be in touch to finalise the details.' Collins's voice stayed cool while at the other end of the phone Frank had lost the power of speech.

'Yeah, yeah, sure, OK,' he mumbled.

'I'm disappointed in you, Frank.' The phone went dead. Frank looked at the receiver for a couple of seconds then stood up. He went into the toilet that led off from his office and vomited.

Rita had left Mavis alone in charge of the shop so that she could nip down to West Croydon and do a bit of shopping. She didn't like Mavis to have the run of the place given her light fingers, but she had to take a break. That morning Rita had refused Mavis another sub on her wages – 'You'll have nothing left come pay day' – and wouldn't put it past her sister just to help herself. She'd counted the float while Mavis nipped out for a sandwich, but there was nothing to stop her selling flowers and pocketing the money instead of ringing it in. But on this particularly brilliant July day, Rita put such cares behind her as she walked down the high street towards the Whitgift Shopping Centre.

The Whitgift had played a part in Rita and Douggie's decision to move to Purley, as Rita needed access to good shops. Stockwell had been fine in the late 1950s and early 1960s because Brixton, just down the road, had some excellent places. But by the late sixties they'd all deteriorated or closed down entirely and she had been forced to endure the long bus journey to the West End. That was all right for Christmas shopping or the kids' birthdays but it was a bit of a palaver for a pair of tights and a lipstick.

Her favourite shop was Allders department store. Every time she went to Croydon she would go and browse in the carpet department simply because she loved the smell of the place so much. When they had first carpeted Foxley Lane the house smelt wonderful for a few weeks until her smoking and the cooking wiped out that lovely aroma of newly woven Axminster fresh off the loom. Something about the smell of new carpet filled Rita with optimism. It stood for new beginnings and everything lovely and clean. But that day she paused only briefly in Carpets before taking the escalator up to Ladies' Fashions on the third floor. She wouldn't normally buy her clothes from Allders, choosing instead the economy of Marks & Spencer or Dotty P's for all but special occasions. But it was sale time and she fancied something decent – like a whole new wardrobe. Frank had not seen all her clothes by any means but if she was going to spend a week with him, everything had to be new.

Rita fingered the bathing costumes, lingerie and summer dresses. She didn't care much for sleeveless slips any more since middle age had gone straight to her upper arms. But there were a few short-sleeved dresses that were smart and would keep her cool, though even some of the sale prices made her whistle between her teeth.

She chose a belted peach shirt-dress, linen skirt and black bathing costume to take to the changing room. As she turned in front of the mirror considering each garment, she had to remind herself that it didn't matter what Douggie would think. It was hard after all those years together to wonder instead how another man might see her. The feeling was at once illicit, painful and exquisite. She decided on all three garments and felt great handing over almost £80 in cash.

One shopping bag naturally led to another. Her appetite now stirred, Rita turned left out of Allders arcade passing the beauty salon where Marilyn had recently got a job, and left again into George Street. From there she could see the silver and white shopfront of Russell & Bromley. Even though she and Douggie had been more than comfortable for years, Rita still had the mentality of a woman with no money – the purchase of shoes from Russell & Bromley was an extravagance.

She was hovering in the doorway looking at the sale rack when she felt someone pinch her bottom. Rita gasped and turned to see Marilyn grinning at her. In her white overall, her hair pulled back in a tight bun and with full make-up, she looked every inch the professional beautician.

'All right Mum, what are you doing bunking off?'

'Oh Christ, Marilyn! Don't do that, you know what my nerves are like. Anyway why aren't you at work?' Rita started, as if she'd been caught in the act of adultery itself.

'Lunch hour, innit? I came out to get a sandwich.' Marilyn waved a white Coughlan's Bakers' bag at her mother. 'What you been buying?' Marilyn wrestled the bag from her mother and pulled out the peach dress.

'Don't start getting stuff out on the street, Marilyn. Leave it alone.' Rita tried to snatch back the dress but Marilyn was now holding it up, having a good look.

'That's nice, Mum, what's it for?'

'Nothing. I just fancied a few bits and pieces.'

'What, from Allders?' Marilyn knew her mother's parsimony with clothes only too well. Rita had things in her wardrobe that had been there almost twenty years, even a pair of brown boots that she'd worn when she was Marilyn's age. Rita would never throw away an item of clothing, preferring to press, dry-clean and repair until the garment died of exhaustion. She was constantly exhorting her daughter to 'Hang your stuff up when you take it off, it lasts longer.'

When Marilyn had finished rifling her mum's remaining purchases she handed the bag back to Rita.

'Blimey, Mum, you'll have to get yourself a boyfriend,' she said teasingly.

'Pardon, madam?'

'Well it's not like Dad ever takes you out any more.'

'Oh yeah, I see what you mean.' Rita relaxed.

'You after shoes as well, then?'

Rita came clean and admitted she was. Marilyn said she'd

help her choose. Her co-operation and Rita's guilt resulted not only in mother getting a new pair of sandals; but daughter too. Rita, despite being careful with money, was occasionally given to sudden fits of generosity with Marilyn and always concluded any purchase for her with the words, 'Right then, that's your lot, don't ask me for anything else for a while.'

Marilyn skipped back to the salon happily swinging her Russell & Bromley bag, but Rita decided that being caught out by her own daughter like that was a very bad sign. She headed for the bus stop. How stupid she had been to think she could get away with enjoying herself.

CHAPTER TWELVE

Please Release Me, Let Me Go . . .

Apart from the absence of their younger son, the last weekend in July started much like any other in the Fisher house, but it would end with a bang. Rita worked at the shop on Saturday and came home at 6.30 p.m., just as Douggie was leaving for the club. They exchanged desultory conversation and Douggie kissed his wife vaguely on his way out of the door. Rita barely noticed. She sat up watching television with Marilyn until nine o'clock, when Marilyn went out dressed to kill without telling her mother where she was going. Everything was as usual.

The night was humid. When Douggie arrived back at 2.30 a.m. Rita was lying wide awake on top of the covers blowing the hair from her fringe trying to keep cool. She heard the front door close and quickly pulled a sheet over herself, pretending to be asleep, just in case her skimpy nightie gave Douggie any ideas. She listened to him tiptoeing around the bedroom undressing and felt his weight sink down on the bed next to her. Involuntarily, she began to grind her teeth. Douggie reached under the sheet and stroked her hips. Rita fought off an urge to scream as he gently lifted her nightdress. When a few minutes of fondling had failed to rouse his wife, Douggie lay on his back and fell into a heavy slumber, his snoring steady and low.

Rita spent most of the night awake trying to remember the last time her husband had bothered to kiss her by way of initiating sex. The night of the Derby had been surprisingly good, but it was a one-off. In recent months the perfunctory nature of Douggie's advances had left Rita feeling unloved and slightly dirty. She imagined it was how a brass felt, with not even the cash at the end to show for it. In her Stockwell days she'd known a couple of tarts from the Angel; nice girls, very clean and adamant that they would never let a punter kiss them. Douggie had always been a smash-and-grab kind of man so the change was not in him, but in her. Was it unreasonable, she wondered, to want to be made love to imaginatively and slowly at her age or was that stuff just for the youngsters? Rita's need for romantic love was no less after twenty-six years of marriage and three children than it had been before a man had ever touched her.

She finally dropped off as dawn was breaking and could barely open her eyes when Douggie woke her at seven with a cup of tea. Even after a late night he rose early, a pattern that Rita had been forced to fall in with during her married life. She dropped back off to sleep letting her tea grow cold, but was awakened half an hour later by the smell of fried breakfast and the sound of Douggie bellowing for her to come and get it.

Rita threw off the covers and stomped down the stairs; she came into the kitchen and snapped, 'Can't I have a bloody lie-in for once? Sunday is the only day I get to please myself.'

'What's the matter with you?' Douggie looked up from his *News of the World*.

'I'm tired, all right, I didn't get any sleep last night.'

'Well you were soundo when I came in, you've had more kip than me.' Douggie went back to slicing bacon and piling it on to the egg and fried bread already poised at the tip of his fork.

Rita stared at her breakfast plate as if she'd never seen a fry-up before in her life. Her appetite was simply not there; gamely she picked up her knife and fork and slowly began to eat, her head down all the while. The last thing she wanted to do was catch his eye, she might explode. Douggie regarded her carefully before starting in with the cheery small-talk.

'I'm gonna nip down the showroom this morning and have a look at the books. Stock's getting a bit low, so I'm going to try and organise for Gully to go down the auctions next weekend.'

'Why can't you go yourself?' Rita was rattled by the thought of Gully going anywhere armed with the company cheque book.

'I've got to pick up some more marble next Saturday, you should see it Reet, it's beautiful, the club's gonna look terrific.'

'Oh yeah.'

'Yeah, we've saved a bloody fortune. The builders seem like nice blokes an' all. When me and Steve got to the club in the lorry they were already there waiting for us. The foreman said to me, "Don't worry about unloading it, Doug, we'll do that, you've done your bit." They were really decent about it. I mean, it's not many builders that can be bothered to get off their arses to help you out, but no, they were there for hours unloading the gear and then storing the marble in the basement and cutting it. They even loaded up the old pallets and shit that was wrapped round them, said they'd get rid of it. Seem like a right nice outfit. I said I might get them to paint the outside of the house while the weather's good. I reckon we should get it done again before winter, what do you think?'

Rita had pulled the colour supplement across the table and opened the front page to read her Stars: *Pluto storms into your love house bringing truth time for all. It's time to honour the deepest desires of your heart. Luck sees a house with a yellow door.*

'What do I think about what?' She looked up irritably.

'Painting the outside of the house this year.'

'Oh I don't care, do what you like.'

Douggie was growing impatient with his wife's mood and wanted to reach across and shake her out of it.

' 'Umpy cow,' he mumbled.

Douggie finished his breakfast in silence then stood up and said, 'Right then, I'm off, I'll be back around lunchtime.' He walked around the kitchen picking up keys and sunglasses, then leaned over the back of his wife's chair to kiss her cheek. As he did so he took the last sausage from her plate and popped it into his mouth, chuckling to himself. Rita didn't find it funny.

'You bloody pig. I'm sick of you, you've got no manners!' She pushed her breakfast plate away, rose furiously from the table and walked over to the windowsill above the sink for her cigarettes. She lit her first fag of the day, her lips shaking and the tears gathering. Douggie looked at her aghast.

'You want to get down the bloody doctor's you do, you're not right.' He slammed the front door on his way out.

Alone in the house, Rita cried freely. It wasn't often she had five minutes to herself and it was a relief to have a really good sob. She wandered out into the garden where an over-cast sky promised another humid day. She sat in her wicker chair and looked at her lovely garden and cried some more. She wished she was unwell, then there would be an easy explanation for the way she felt. But even if there was a pill that could cure her ills she wasn't sure she'd want to take it. Then she would have to carry on for the rest of her life going through the same routine. Rita had to come clean at least with herself and admit she was bored.

For months, she had been reciting the usual female palli-atives to herself: count your blessings, you've got your health, you haven't got any money worries and none of your kids are in trouble with the law. But freedom from strife was no con-solation. She was bored with Douggie, bored with the shop, the house, pissed off with never going out and always beset by the feeling that she was missing out, that there was a better life out there somewhere. And now she was beginning to gather evidence that there well might be. She wondered what her mum would say if she'd lived to see this day.

Rita had thought a lot about her mum recently. Compared to Rita's, Lillian's life had been scarred by dreadful hardships. Of the six children she bore only three survived beyond childhood, two taken by pneumonia as infants, the third burnt to death in a car. There had been many other pregnancies that never came to term through either miscarriage or the abortionist who would come round to the flat, fiddle about at the end of the bed for ten minutes, then leave Lillian to bleed the dead foetus into a bucket.

Rita could remember her mum lying in bed with the bloody bucket beside her, begging Rita to take a day off school to look after her. But Rita loved school and at the age of eleven couldn't understand why her father couldn't come home to take care of her mum. Rita's father Arthur was not a likeable sort. A big drinker, he would beat her mother and rob the little money she'd been able to earn from cleaning and leaflet-dropping. Rita was constantly having to drag her father out of the pub to beg the price of a pint of milk or a loaf of bread, which he would have to hand over, grudgingly, because of the presence of other men. He had the newspaper stand by Clapham Common tube station, a cover which enabled him to run a book and take bets in the days before betting shops were licensed. Compared to her mum, Rita had an easy life, a good life she should be grateful for. That wasn't much of a consolation either.

Rita took a bath and after dressing and putting on a load of washing, she decided to sort out her handbag. She chucked out the broken cigarettes, paper clips, bits of floristry ribbon and an old lipstick, the remains of which she'd been digging out with her finger for weeks. She assembled the loose pages from her address book and stuck them back in with Sellotape. She rinsed her comb under the tap and wiped it dry with a teatowel. Old receipts were glanced at and then torn. Lastly, she opened the zip of the inside compartment of her bag and took out the white envelope she had secreted there for almost a week.

It was a letter from Frank addressed to her at the shop. In it he told her that he'd made enquiries and found out that Dolly and Bill now ran a pub called the Sandpiper about two miles along the coast from Margate. He was free to go any time after the first Saturday in August, the following week. He suggested they drive down on the Saturday night and stay for a few days, but thought it best that she rang Dolly first and squared it with her.

Rita stared at his handwriting. Despite all appearances to the contrary and a lot of polishing over the years, it betrayed a man of poor education. Won over as women often are by men's weaknesses and not their strengths, this chink in his armour had touched Rita. That he'd bothered to write a letter at all and reveal himself when he could just have phoned was more romance than she was accustomed to.

Rita stroked the letter with the tip of her finger, tracing his signature at the bottom several times before folding it and placing it back in its envelope. Then she zipped it up in her handbag. She had reflected a great deal on his character in recent weeks and decided that beyond mutual attraction they had something crucial in common. Both were trapped in marriages that no longer sustained them, and both were young enough to start again. She would be mad to not even spend a couple of days with him and see how they got on. Maybe he was right, maybe they had always been destined to wind up together. It was true that he had done some terrible things when he was younger, but he had admitted to her that he had acted out of panic. And as he said, we all make mistakes, don't we?

Rita rang Directory Enquiries and found the number of the Sandpiper. She looked at her watch: 11.15, which meant that Dolly would be setting up the bar for the Sunday lunch session. Would Dolly still put cheese and salty nibbles out on the bar like she used to for Sunday lunches in the Angel?

The phone rang for a long time and Rita was beginning to think she'd dialled the wrong number when a smoky, slightly breathless and impatient voice answered, 'The Sandpiper.' The timbre had grown deeper with the years, but it was unmistakable nonetheless.

'Hello stranger,' Rita chuckled.

'Who's that?' Dolly asked.

'You couldn't lend us a few bob till the weekend could you, Doll?'

Dolly hesitated for a few seconds. 'That's not you is it, Rita?'

'Course it's me, you silly mare.'

'No way! How are you, love?'

'Fed up, Doll.'

Rita told her everything. They spoke for half an hour, their conversation interrupted several times by Bill asking his wife if she intended doing any work that day. Dolly put him straight: 'Sod off Bill, I'm talking.'

Dolly murmured sympathetically for the most part, pausing only for a sharp intake of breath when Rita reached the bit about Frank. 'He's not still about, is he?' Rita filled her in on the last few months, explaining how Frank had changed. Dolly, not given much to romance, commented, 'Yeah well I suppose you two always did have the hots for each other and if you say he's got a few bob . . .'

'It's more than that, Dolly.'

'If you say so, love.'

When Rita heard Douggie's car in the drive she whispered unnecessarily, 'Dolly, he's back, I'll have to shoot off. But I'll call you in the week yeah, let you know when we're arriving.'

'Rita?'

'What?'

'Go steady, eh?'

Douggie opened the door to find Rita placing the receiver back on its cradle. 'Who was that?' he asked.

'Mind your own business.'

'You've cheered up, then.'

This was witty for Douggie but Rita bristled at his sarcasm and stomped into the kitchen. Douggie stood in the doorway and watched her take the washing out of the machine. He looked around the kitchen for signs of lunch but found none. Rita always cooked a Sunday lunch. He stepped outside where she was now standing with her laundry basket and asked tentatively, 'We eating then, or what?'

'Help yourself. There's plenty of food in the fridge.' She didn't look up at him.

Douggie bit his tongue and, eschewing his usual cans of bitter, went to the cocktail cabinet in the front room and poured himself a good four fingers of Scotch. If there was going to be a row he wanted to be ready for it.

'Cor, it's bloody hot,' he said to nobody and opened the french windows that led from the front room to the patio. Rita hung the washing out to dry while Douggie stood with one hand in his pocket, the other fist clutched around his glass. Neither of them wanted to fire the first shot. The sky was overcast and grey and the air was perfectly still; they both wished for rain.

The silence and the damp heat became oppressive. Douggie was so wound up he thought he might blow and Rita was biting back tears, her throat thick with hopelessness. He looked at her and was about to speak when they heard the front door opening. Marilyn came in.

'Mum!' she called.

'Out here.' Poor Marilyn. Unusually light-hearted after a wonderful night, she had no warning of what was waiting for her.

'Where have you been all night?' Douggie barked at his daughter. It wasn't like her dad to be in a bad mood, it was usually her mum.

'Round Nelson's,' she answered carefully.

'You seeing that fucking nig-nog again?'

That did it. Rita turned quickly and spat at her husband: 'You're bloody ignorant you are, just like your mother was.'

'What's my mum got to do with anything?'

'She was a bigot as well.'

'Don't you talk about my mum like that.' Douggie's voice was threatening.

'Well, it's true. She was an ignorant old bitch, your mum, and you're no better.'

'Now hang about . . .' Douggie pointed at his wife, who stood opposite him about five feet away.

Marilyn glanced nervously between the two and tried to placate her father. 'Dad,' she pleaded, 'he's really nice and you know it wasn't him who gave me those drugs, I told you.'

'Yeah but you never told me who did give you drugs, did you, and if it had been anybody at the club I'd have found out about it by now. You're a lying little cow, Marilyn, and you're a slut as well.'

'Don't you dare call my daughter a slut!'

'Well what else do you call girls like her? She could have been going out with Mark, but nice normal blokes aren't enough for little tarts like her, she has to have a macaroon. Next thing you know she'll be pregnant and living in a little flat on the dole like all the other tarts.'

Marilyn was going to have to put her indignation on hold in order to stop a big row going off. Her mum and dad always argued, but not like this. They really looked like they hated each other. Her mum, especially, looked like she could kill.

'What do you think it's like for her, eh?' Rita pointed to

her daughter. 'Can't even bring her boyfriend home to meet her dad because he's such a racist bastard. I'd be ashamed of you as well if I was her. In fact, Douggie, I'm ashamed of you anyway, because you're nothing better than a pig.'

'Stop it, you two. Mum leave it. It doesn't matter.' Marilyn's voice was breaking. Douggie's face coloured alarmingly and the veins in his neck stuck out. His knuckles around the glass turned white and it was all he could do not to lash out at her. Instead he threw his glass down on to the patio, where it smashed.

'We might as well pack it in then if that's what you think, get a divorce.' In the past, the mere mention of the word from either of them had been enough to silence the other into submission. It was something they said they would never do. But Rita merely looked at him for a few seconds wondering where all the love had gone.

'It's probably for the best,' she said calmly.

Marilyn's voice wobbled a plea. 'Stoppit you two, you don't mean it. Mum, tell him you don't mean it.'

'It's too late, Marilyn, I've had it up to here. I'm fed up with everything. Him, you, this house, the shop, I've had enough.' Rita stormed back into the house.

'Mum, where are you going?'

'Out.' The front door slammed.

'Dad! Go on, go and get her back.'

'Sod your mother. She's not the only one who's fed up. It's not much of a life for me either having to come home to her long boat every day. Miserable cow, I should have packed me bags ages ago.' Douggie pulled aside the net curtain and stepped inside, where he fixed himself another Scotch. Marilyn fought off waves of panic.

'I'll make lunch, eh Dad? That'll cheer her up.'

'Nothing'll cheer her up. She's permanently pissed off, your mother.'

'Oh, Dad, go and get her, go and make up.'

'Mind your own business, Marilyn. You want to get your own life sorted out. This is between me and your mother. If she wants a divorce she can bloody well have one.' Douggie downed his Scotch and looked at his daughter with tears rolling down her face. 'Bloody hell, not you as well. I'm going down the pub.'

Rita walked back into the house at half-past two, calmer but with no loss of resolve, to be greeted by the smell of Sunday lunch. She went into the kitchen and found the table all beautifully set with best linen, glasses and the fancy cruet set she only used for special occasions. Marilyn was pouring batter mixture into little patty tins.

'I didn't know you knew how to make Yorkshires, love.'

'Oh, hello Mum. Well I've watched you often enough, but I couldn't get the bloody lumps out.'

Rita looked at her daughter with affection. How funny it was that normally they were at each other's throats, but now with Ronnie away, she felt closer to Marilyn. She was a funny kid. A lazy, stroppy little mare for the most part, she would nonetheless rally and do things around the house if Rita and Doug ever rowed. She'd put on loads of washing and dust the front room, like it was going to make any difference to how her parents felt about one another.

'Where's your father?'

'Down the pub.'

Marilyn looked at her mum warily. 'You didn't mean it, did you, about getting divorced?'

Rita sighed and lowered herself on to a chair, careful to keep her elbows off Marilyn's carefully set table.

'I don't know, love. We're not happy though, we haven't been for ages.' They both looked out of the kitchen window at the first rumble of thunder. 'I'd better get my washing in.'

Rita pulled clothes quickly from the line as the first heavy drops started to fall. Some of the washing was still damp. She dumped the basket as she came into the kitchen and went to the cupboard under the stairs to get the clothes horse, then said, 'Sod it' and kicked the basket into a corner. 'Shall we open a bottle of wine, then?' she asked Marilyn.

They waited until three and ate without Douggie. Rita was relieved that he hadn't come back, Marilyn crestfallen. She dished up three plates and placed a saucepan lid over her father's, putting it in the oven on gas mark ¼ like she'd seen Rita do so many times. The beef was dry and the Yorkshires underdone, but Rita ate enthusiastically, complimenting her daughter on the first Sunday dinner she'd cooked all on her own. Did a daughter reach some kind of watershed when she cooked her first roast? Rita wondered. The final signal of her readiness to enter the world as a grown woman. She looked at Marilyn's young face, all worried. How would her kids take it, if she split from their dad? Of course, none of them were children any more in the strictest sense, so they ought not to be wounded by the breaking up of the home. Or was she wrong about that? She told herself she'd cross that bridge when she came to it.

After lunch Marilyn went to her room and Rita dozed on the sofa, listening to the rain falling in great sheets beyond the french windows. As she slept fitfully she dreamed of their dog, Sinatra, who'd died the year before. Sinatra was an old mongrel that Douggie had bought from a man in a pub in Croydon when they first moved to Foxley Lane. The man said the council were transferring him to a flat in a high-rise and that he wasn't allowed to take the dog with him. Although Rita had always previously put her foot down, saying she didn't want pets for the simple reason that she'd be the one who'd get stuck with looking after them, she'd been quite taken by Sinatra when he came back from the pub with Douggie. The kids went on and on and on about keeping him, promising that they would feed and walk him and finally she had to relent.

After a cautious beginning, Sinatra and Rita formed the strongest tie, probably because, as anticipated, Rita did most of the feeding and walking. Their bond was cemented the first time it stormed with Sinatra in the house. He cowered by her legs under the kitchen table and shadowed her around the house. He shook and whimpered and Rita had to hold him like a baby until the storm died down. She complained about him constantly, his hairs everywhere and digging up her flowerbeds, but secretly she liked the way he never let her out of his sight. She was lonely for months after he was run over by the milk float – he'd crawled under the front wheels in pursuit of next door's cat and the milkman hadn't seen them. The cat got away, of course.

Rita was woken by the sound of keys jangling and opened her eyes to see Douggie swaying at the end of the sofa, obviously drunk. His tone was contrite: 'I've been thinking.'

'Don't strain yourself.'

'No, listen, don't start, I've been thinking that we should go away, take a holiday. Leave the kids, just me and you.' Douggie slumped by Rita's feet. Rita said nothing. 'I thought we could go next weekend after I've been to Andover. What do you think?'

'I've made arrangements for next weekend.' She couldn't look at him.

'What arrangements?'

'I'm going down to the coast to see Dolly, I spoke to her this morning.' Rita yawned and looked around for her fags.

'What – Angel Dolly?' asked Douggie, surprised. Rita nodded.

'Who with?'

'Nobody.'

'Well, I'll come with you, then.'

'I don't want you to. I want to go on my own.'

'You never go anywhere on your own.'

'Well maybe it's time I started.' She looked at Douggie's face, full of defeat and Dewars. 'I just need a break from everything, Douggie. Don't take it personally.'

'Don't take it personally! You said you wanted a divorce earlier.' His voice rose.

'You brought it up.'

'You pushed me.'

'Oh stop it, there's no point us going on like this, we're just going round in circles. We need a break, Douggie. It might be helpful if you moved out.' Douggie laughed uproariously at this one.

'You're having a laugh. If you think I'm leaving my house you've got another think coming. I'm staying right here in my bed, in my house. If you don't like it, you go.'

That night, Rita moved a few of her things into Ronnie's room and the war of attrition began in earnest. Douggie would crack first, she figured. He'd never been able to handle an atmosphere and would apologise even when he was in the right, to break a stalemate. But she hadn't bargained on the depth of Douggie's hurt, nor his determination to grind *her* down for once in their married life. Neither slept well that night and they woke up on the Monday ill-prepared for the longest week of their lives.

CHAPTER THIRTEEN

Unlucky for Some

Rita fought depression by keeping busy. She spent the first few evenings of that week going through cupboards and wardrobes, chucking out junk and sorting clothes into bags for the charity shops. Hardly bothering to eat, she survived on adrenalin, staying up until 1 or 2 a.m., folding and packing items she had hoarded for years. If she did end up moving on, she wanted to travel light. She had a wobbly moment on the Tuesday evening when she came across a suitcase full of baby clothes that she had kept for any grandchildren that might come along. The knitted matinée coats and bootees had been made by her mother, the christening gowns seemed elaborate and old-fashioned compared to the casual wear favoured by mothers now. The tiny garments brought back vivid memories of happier times. She felt regretful but refused to give in to tears for fear that they would never stop.

Wednesday evening had passed off pleasantly. Rita could relax knowing that Douggie wouldn't bother coming here before his shift at the club.

Marilyn came home from work and said that she was thinking about getting a flat with Nelson. They sat in the lounge and worked their way through two bottles of wine and a big box of Twiglets while Rita dispensed advice. Marilyn explained that she thought it might make things easier for her mum and dad if she wasn't about. Rita tried to reassure her that her presence made no difference to relations between her and her dad – in fact it probably made it a bit easier: at least there was somebody in the house they could talk to. But she wasn't a kid any more and if she was sure she wanted to move in with him, then she should.

'So will you split the bills and rent down the middle, then?' Rita knew that Nelson was a student. She didn't want Marilyn to be lumbered with the role of provider at her age. At any age. She couldn't stand men who let women pay for them, and there were too many of those kind around these days for her liking. No pride.

'Yeah, course, fifty-fifty.'

'Do yourself a favour, love.'

'What's that, Mum?'

'Always make sure you've got a little bit of money they don't know about.' Rita tapped the side of her nose conspiratorially.

'Why's that?'

'Just in case. Oh and by the way . . .'

'Yeah?'

'I'd like to meet him first, madam. And make sure you go on the pill.'

Douggie divided his time between the showroom and the club, making a nuisance of himself in both places. He was sharp with Vivienne, finding fault with everything she did. Steve had to take her to one side and explain that his mum and dad were having trouble and to please just be patient. Marilyn had called him at home and told him all about the things that had been said on the Sunday. He didn't bring it up with his dad. It was better just to keep his head down and ride it out. He had no real fears of a permanent rift between his parents – they were the most solid couple he'd ever come across. And as he said to his sister, 'It's not like there's anybody else involved. Just let them sort it out.'

Douggie would go straight to the club after closing the showroom and drink steadily until it was time to close. He stopped bothering to cash off the tills, simply stuffing the money into bags and locking it in the safe. Not wanting to challenge Douggie himself, Mark called his father and filled him in. Mark was pretty sure that Douggie didn't have a clue about his involvement with Marilyn's sudden departure from the club. But you could never know for sure and fathers were funny about their daughters anyway. Something had clearly put Douggie's nose out of joint and Mark didn't want to be the touchpaper that set off an outburst.

On Wednesday evening, Frank turned up at the club to see for himself what was going on and Douggie made the mistake of confiding in him.

After a rush when they first opened, the club was quiet. Just a few of the tables were occupied and only six or seven drinkers stood at the bar. It was only 10 p.m. and the rest of the night stretched ahead seemingly without end. Frank hovered at a distance from Douggie, pretending to busy himself with paperwork at his favourite table at the back, watching him closely, before he made his approach. Douggie was leaning, almost slumped, on the bar when Frank put a hand on his shoulder.

'What's up, mate? You look like a wet blanket.'

'She says she wants a divorce.' Douggie drained his Scotch and waved his glass at the barman.

'I wish Doreen would ask me for a divorce.' Douggie didn't find the quip amusing and merely snorted, forcing Frank to try another approach. 'She's just breaking your balls, mate, all wives do it. Besides, I thought you two were tight.'

'So did I.'

'There's no one else, is there?' Pissed as he was, Douggie could never have detected the subtle wavering in Frank's voice.

'Another bloke? My Rita? Not in a million years, mate. It's not her style. She's a pain in the arse, but she's no slag.' Douggie stared off into space for a minute, watched carefully by Frank. 'She's going away on her own this weekend to see an old mate. I mean, on her own.' Douggie shook his head disbelievingly. 'She never goes anywhere on her own. Do you remember Dolly and Bill from the Angel?' Frank nodded. 'She's off to see her.'

'She told you where she was going, then?' Frank's voice rose a few notches in surprise.

'Yeah, why shouldn't she? We're still married.'

'No reason.' Frank took a deep breath. 'Look Doug, why don't you take a couple of weeks off? I know it's difficult when you've got problems indoors but you can't keep getting pissed in here. Sooner or later the punters will start to notice and you're not keeping on top of the bookwork. It's not on really, mate.'

'This fucking place was the start of it. She never wanted me to come in with you, did you know that?'

'No, I didn't.'

'I might as well jack it in. I'm kidding myself really. Old swinger like me doesn't belong in a nightclub, I should be at home getting on her nerves.'

'Don't be hasty, Doug.' Frank was interrupted by the arrival of his son at the table.

'Dad, someone to see you.'

'They'll have to wait.'

'It's Collins. I've put him on your table at the back.' Frank blanched but didn't turn around.

'What the fuck is he doing here?'

'He don't look too happy.'

'Shit.' Frank ran his hands through his hair and tried to think. It was all unravelling.

'What's the matter, you owe the geezer money or something?' Douggie said too loudly and laughed.

'Stay there, Doug, don't move. I'll be back in a minute.'

Frank walked slowly and coolly over to the table where Collins sat with two associates, a relaxed smile on his face.

Not particularly distinctive in appearance, there were no outward signs that these were men to be feared. They were noticeable only because none of them were drinking. Frank offered to fetch some drinks, but Collins put his hand up to silence him.

'I'm not here to socialise, Frank, I'll come straight to the point. I'm not very happy with your decision to go back on our agreement. If you can't handle the business, you shouldn't have wasted my time.' He paused, then said, 'I hate it when people waste my time. However, on this occasion I don't see that I have any choice but to go along with it.'

Unused to being spoken down to, Frank fidgeted uncomfortably.

'It was damage limitation,' he said. 'My hands are tied. If I'd let it go on, things could have got messy. I hadn't bargained on the weak link in my chain. I admit it was an error of judgement, but I don't think you can accuse me of wasting your time.'

Collins regarded Frank coldly. 'I think you'll find I can do whatever I like, Frank.' The two cronies laughed loyally. Collins directed his gaze into the corner where Douggie was loudly urging Eimar to sing 'Danny Boy'. 'Your weak link, I presume?'

'No, he's just a punter.' Frank coughed.

'This is all very unfortunate, Frank, very unfortunate.' To his credit, Frank didn't flinch, just waited for Collins to finish. 'You take delivery of the second shipment on Saturday morning as agreed. At three o'clock one of my boys will be round to collect. He'll be expecting to pick up £200,000.'

'Hold on a minute.' Frank's composure started to slip. 'We agreed that I'd give you seventy-five grand for each shipment and that I'd have a month after delivery to offload it and settle up. You're asking for another fifty and no time to pay. It's not what we agreed.'

'We agreed to nine consecutive shipments: you're bottling out after two. There are penalties for loss of business, Frank.' The two cronies nodded gravely. 'Anyway, I'd have thought a man of your means could lay your hands on that kind of money without too much trouble.'

'I can. But it's not what we agreed.' Frank was accustomed to setting his own terms. He wasn't adjusting well to the boot being on the other foot.

It was perhaps not the best of times for Douggie to introduce himself. He'd grown bored at the bar and looked around for Frank. His curiosity piqued, he wandered none too steadily over to the table and offered his hand to Collins.

'Douggie Fisher, I'm Frank's partner. You not drinking then, you lot?'

'Nice to meet you, Douggie.' Collins shook his hand but did not offer his own name. He glanced at Frank and raised his eyebrows. Only the twitching of the muscles around Frank's jaw betrayed his agony.

Numbed by Dewars, Douggie was oblivious to the atmosphere. He slapped Collins on the back heartily.

'Have a drink, go on. You can't sit in our club and not have a drink. It's in the rules isn't it, Frank? No, I don't want no arguments, I'll get us a bottle of bubbly.'

While Douggie weaved unsteadily over to the bar, Collins and his henchmen stood up. Collins stood very close to Frank and whispered, 'Interesting company you keep, Frank. We'll see you Saturday.' The three men were laughing as they walked away. By the time Douggie returned to the table with a bottle and five glasses they were nowhere to be seen.

'Thanks a fucking lot.' Frank had murder in his eyes.

'What? I only offered them a drink.'

'Look, when I'm in conference you stay out, do you understand?'

Douggie mimicked his partner: '*When I'm in conference* . . .

What are you, the fucking Prime Minister?' A couple at the next table fell quiet, the better to hear the unfolding disagreement. Frank held his finger up to his lips to shush him but Douggie didn't care who was listening. 'Anyway we're supposed to be partners. If it's business, I should know about it.' He popped the cork on the bottle and eased his indigestion simultaneously. Frank reeled from the alcoholic fumes of the belch. He didn't know if his temper could hold. They stared at one another. Douggie's watery eyes tried to fix Frank's defiantly, but he knew he was beaten. After a brief stand-off, Frank told him:

'This club represents only a fraction of my business interests. If I want to talk in my own place, I will. When you're needed I'll let you know.'

From the end of the bar, Mark had kept a watchful eye on his dad and Douggie. He wanted to know what Collins had wanted and what Douggie had said to him to make him get up and leave like that. At a loss to know what to do for the best, he bolted to the office to refresh himself.

Douggie slumped lower in his chair, resignation written all over his face. He knew he didn't belong at the club.

'Look Frank, you don't need me here, Rita never wanted me here, I'm a cunt for even thinking I could make a go of it. Steve's not really interested, he just turns up out of loyalty to me and Marilyn got herself into trouble in the first five minutes.'

Frank had squeezed the full story from Mark and wondered how much Douggie really knew.

Douggie went on: 'There's no point, Frank. I might as well jack it in. How soon can you give me my money back?'

Two demands for payment in one night. Frank had had better evenings. 'As soon as I can find another partner to buy your share.' He tried to stall.

'Oh come on, Frank. Twenty grand is loose change to you.'

'Let me see what I can do.' He inhaled deeply. 'So when do you want to finish?'

'Now's as good a time as any.'

'But I need you to go to Andover for me on Saturday.'

'Get someone else. I'm going to find Rita on the coast at the weekend. She might cheer up with a bit of fresh air, I might be able to talk to her.'

'Just let her be for a while, Doug, you might find with a couple of days away she starts to miss you a bit.' Douggie thought about this. Frank continued: 'Anyway, I can't get anybody else to do it. The shipment's in your name. Only you can collect.' Frank had knotted the wire from the champagne bottle so tightly around his fingers that it was starting to cut off his circulation.

'You take the piss, you really do. I'm just a lackey for you like all the others, aren't I? It's all bollocks this talk of us being partners. Why did you want me to come here in the first place? It's not like you need my money, is it, Frank?'

'I told you, Doug, I needed somebody I could trust, the place was being stripped by the old manager and staff – but Mark's got it more or less under control now.'

Several tables away a girl shrieked as a glass tumbled to the floor and shattered. Frank flinched. 'And I want you to go early to Southampton. The builders are going to be here at midday and they want to get cracking, get all the marble cut and measured up – if they can get started early enough, they'll have the new bar on in time for opening on Saturday night. Have you sorted out the van yet?'

'No, I haven't, but Gully reckons there's an old Bedford flat-bed knocking about that we can use. But that's your lot, mate. After that I'm done.' Douggie rose, ready to go. He extended a sweaty hand to Frank.

'No hard feelings, eh?'

Frank studied Douggie's face and put a matey arm around his shoulder. 'Bit of advice Doug,' he said.

'What's that then?'

'Let Rita cool down, eh? Don't go chasing her at the weekend. There's no harm done if she wants to see an old mate, is there?'

'You're probably right. Fucking women.'

CHAPTER FOURTEEN

Better the Devil You Know

Saturday morning was as glorious as any of the summer. The early sun streamed through the lightweight curtains in Ronnie's room and Rita rose at about 5.30 to make herself a cup of tea and take it back to bed. Her belly fluttering with excitement, she doubted she would be able to get back to sleep.

She met Douggie in the kitchen dressed and ready to go to Andover. The hostility between them had been replaced by a mute numbness.

'What you doing up so early?' She wasn't really interested.

'I'm off to Andover to pick up the last of the marble. Steve will be here in a minute.'

'Oh, right.'

Rita squeezed the teabag on the side of her mug and put it in the rubbish bin. Douggie looked at her sleep-tousled hair and puffy face. She'd been such a cow to him recently he didn't know whether to kiss her or slap her chops. He was going to tell her when he got back from Southampton but in case he missed her he wanted her to know now.

'I've jacked the club in,' he said. Rita froze. He must know about her and Frank.

'Why?' She tried to keep her voice calm and not look at him.

'I thought you'd be pleased.'

'Yeah, but why?'

'Because I'm a dopey sod who should have stayed well away. You were right, Rita, I don't belong in a nightclub.

I'm just an old prat.'

'Nothing's happened, has it?' Rita kept stirring her tea even though she hadn't put any sugar in it. 'You haven't fallen out with Frank?'

'No, no, nothing like that. I reckon I'll have a job getting my money out of the place though.'

'I still don't understand why.' Rita was terrified that she was missing the subtext.

'Because I thought it would make you happy.' Douggie looked down at his shoes. The doorbell rang. 'There's Steve, I'd better get cracking. I'll be back around one or two. Will I see you before you go?' he asked carefully.

'I'm not sure what train I'm getting yet, I was going to leave mid-afternoon, so yeah, maybe.'

He kissed her lightly on the cheek. 'If I don't see you, have a lovely time.' Douggie turned back on the doorstep and gave a little wave that made her stomach lurch. She rushed to the window in the dining room to watch him reverse the dirty old lorry out of the drive on to Foxley Lane. Trust Douggie to turn up trumps just at the wrong moment.

When he'd called her at the shop on Thursday, Frank said he would pick her up outside East Croydon station at five o'clock. He would be in and out of the club during the day, doing last-minute jobs. He wasn't sure how long he'd have to hang around with the builders, but with any luck they'd be in Margate in time for dinner.

Rita thought hard. The last time Douggie had been to the club was Wednesday, so Frank must have known when he called her on Thursday that Douggie was pulling out. Why didn't he say anything to her? Feeling anxious and unsettled, she forced herself through her routine, ironing and packing her clothes and taking a bath. She had to pop into the shop about noon to see how Mavis was getting on and make sure she would be all right for cashing up and opening again on

Monday. That and a few other bits in the house, then she'd call a cab to East Croydon. She hoped that Douggie wouldn't offer her a lift. Maybe she should take her case with her to the shop and leave straight from there.

At about 10.30 she had just got out of the bath and was putting her hair in rollers when she heard the front door open. It couldn't be Marilyn because she was at the salon and if it was Douggie, he was back early. She pulled her dressing gown around her and as she reached the landing a young man's voice shouted up the stairs:

'Mum? Dad? Anybody in?'

'Ronnie!'

Rita flew down the stairs two at a time and found her tanned boy waiting with a big grin on his face, looking if anything taller than when he went away. 'Hello love, you're back early, I thought you were going to stay out there until the end of the summer. Come on, I'll put the kettle on.' She pointed at his suitcase: 'And I suppose that's full of dirty washing.'

Ronnie grinned at her so she playfully slapped him. 'Bring it in the kitchen, we might as well get it in the machine while the sun's shining.'

'Where's Dad? Gone to work?' Ronnie walked around the kitchen looking at everything, trying to see if there had been any changes.

'Yeah, he's had to go to Andover to pick up some marble or something for the club. He said he'd be back about one or two o'clock.' They both glanced at the clock on the kitchen wall which said twenty to eleven. 'So how come you're home? Run out of money?' Rita chuckled.

'No. Marilyn rang me on Tuesday. Said that you and Dad had a row and that you were getting a divorce. I wanted to find out what was going on.' He heaped four sugars in his tea. 'Got any biscuits, Mum?'

Rita gulped and went to the cupboard to get the biscuit

tin. How much love could she take in one day? First Douggie, now Ronnie. She was starting to go into a tailspin. She could hardly go away now that Ronnie was home.

'Ronnie love, don't worry about me and your father, we're going through a bad patch. I don't know what's going to happen, but whatever happens you'll be all right.'

'Yeah but are you going to get a divorce?'

She looked at her son's face, so worried, and said softly, 'I don't know. Anyway, I'll talk to you in a minute, let me just go and get dressed.'

Rita picked up the phone in her bedroom and dialled the number of the club. It rang and rang without answer so she dialled again in case she'd pushed the wrong buttons the first time, but still nobody picked up. She couldn't call Frank at home and though she knew that he had a phone in his car, she didn't know his number. She'd have to keep trying until he got there.

While Rita was trying to track down Frank, Douggie and Steve had a more immediate problem with the Bedford. The back axle had given way on the M3 around Bracknell and the van had slid on to the hard shoulder, shedding its load of pallets in a twenty-yard stream.

'Piece of fucking shit,' said Douggie kicking the van. 'I told Gully it couldn't take the weight, he was like "Oh no, it'll be all right, sound as a pound." Bloody idiot.'

'Do you think the marble's broken, Dad?' Steve looked down the motorway where the pallets were strewn along the hard shoulder.

'How should I know? Look, you stay here with the van, I'll get a lift to a phone and ring Gully, get him to sort out another motor.' Douggie looked at his watch. 'Bloody hell, it's half-eleven, I'm supposed to be there to let the builders in at twelve. Frank said he might not be able to get there until after lunch. Gully's going to have to take the spare keys up town to let them in. They won't hang about, you know. If we don't turn up, they'll just piss off.'

'Oh sod the builders, Dad. There's nothing we can do about it. Get us a cup of tea while you're at the services.'

Douggie stood at the side of the road with his thumb out, frowning at his son who had stripped off his shirt and was lying on the grass verge getting a suntan. He only had to wait about five minutes before a Water Board van drew up. Douggie explained quickly what had happened and jumped in, giving the driver a thumbs-up signal. He was at the nearest services within ten minutes, but had to wait another six or seven, while Vivienne went to get Gully from his basement. Douggie kept shoving tenpence pieces in the phone and making apologetic gestures to the man from the Water Board who'd offered to drive him back to the van when he'd finished. When Gully finally came on the line, he took the full blast of Douggie's fury.

'You get on to Billy Gaines and you get him to get one of his drivers down to us on the M3, and in the meantime move your greasy arse double quick and make sure you're at that club for twelve to let the builders in. The spare keys are in my desk drawer, all right?'

'Yeah all right, keep your hair on, I'll do it.' Gully gave the phone back to Vivienne and said to her with a smirk, 'I'll sort a van and driver out for him, but the fucking builders can wait, I'm going to finish this Escort first.' Gully's watch said noon.

'Another hour or so won't hurt 'em.' Vivienne rolled her eyes but said nothing. It was between those two, she wasn't getting involved.

Meanwhile, in Poland Street four men were waiting in a van. They wore builders' overalls, but were not planning to do much in the line of construction that day. They watched the club and waited. Unknown to them, twenty yards further down the street, a Ford Granada with three men inside was also waiting. They'd been parked up since 11 a.m. It was a very hot day and tempers were short. Nobody likes to be kept waiting in the heat.

Rita had hung out the first load of washing and was ready to take out her rollers. She went upstairs and tried calling again. Still no reply. She couldn't just stand him up; she had to explain. She'd try again from the shop, but if there was still no answer she'd have to go up to the club and leave a note or something. Douggie should be making his way back about now, so she reckoned it was probably safe.

In her bedroom she unpacked her case and hung her new clothes back in the wardrobe. She stroked the peach shirt-dress. 'Shame,' she said to herself. Ronnie was in his bed-room playing records, Rita winced at the noise and screamed at him to 'turn that bloody thing down'. She told him she had to pop out for a couple of hours, check on the shop and so on. He was to tell his father that she'd be back mid-after-noon. If he wanted to make himself useful, he could scrub down the barbecue while she was out and go to the butcher's and get some steaks and sausages.

'Anything else, your ladyship?' Ronnie was reclining on his bed.

'Yes. Ring your sister at work and tell her I want her home for dinner tonight. She can bring her boyfriend if she likes. The number's in my red book downstairs and don't you stay on the phone all bloody afternoon talking to your mates.'

'Mum?'

'What?'

'You're not really going to get a divorce, are you?'

She thought about it for a few seconds, then said, 'I shouldn't think so, love. But don't you start getting involved, I'll talk to your father later.'

Ronnie stood up. Towering over his mother, he put his

arms around her and lifted her up.

'Get off, you big lump, I've just done my make-up.'

Rita closed the door behind her and just caught a bus that was coming down Foxley Lane. The Saturday afternoon traffic was heavy and she didn't get to the shop until about one. She chatted to her sister for ten minutes, mostly about Ronnie's homecoming, and slipped out the back a couple of times to use the phone. No answer. She hung about until 1.30 and tried one last time.

'Who you trying to get hold of?' Mavis asked her.

'Nothing. I was just going to ask Ronnie to switch the washing machine on. He probably can't hear with his records blaring. Anyway Mave, I'd better get a move on. See you next week.'

She boarded a train at East Croydon and by 2 p.m. was at Victoria station deliberating whether to get a taxi or just jump on the tube. The queue for taxis was almost out of the station and traffic looked solid, so she took the tube to Oxford Circus and walked the five minutes to Poland Street.

As she drew closer to the club, her nerve failed her; telling Frank that she wasn't going to Margate wasn't the problem, it was meaning it when she told him that it would be for the best if they never saw one another again. Stalling for time, she made a quick detour into Marks and bought some new socks and underpants for Douggie by way of a peace offering. He would be at home by now; seeing Ronnie would really cheer him up.

Frank arrived at the club at around 1.30, to find it locked up and in darkness. From outside he could hear the phone going. Douggie should have dropped the gear by now, where was he? He looked up and down the street until he saw the builders' van and looked questioningly at the driver, who simply shrugged and tapped his watch to show his impatience. He let himself in, turned on the lights and went downstairs to the office where he put a large clothing holdall with £170,000 in cash under the desk. He figured on there being about ten grand in the safe and Collins could whistle for the rest. He was getting more than he was owed.

On the hard shoulder of the M3 near Bracknell father and son were snapping at one another. Steven was slouched in the passenger seat of the van with his feet up on the dash.

'What time's this van supposed to be turning up? It's half-past two already. I'm supposed to take Shelley to Brockwell Park this afternoon. Three and a half hours we've been stuck here.'

'I don't know, do I? Billy will get a driver to me as soon as he's got one; he won't let me down, he's a mate. Besides, he can't. He hasn't paid me for his wife's Toyota yet.'

'I do not understand why it's us that has to go to Andover anyway. If his mate has got the haulage firm, why doesn't he just get him to haul it to the club? He takes the piss out of you, Dad.'

'Yeah well not for much longer, I'm jacking it in.' Steven sat up straight and turned to look at his father.

'When did all this come about?'

'Oh, I been thinking about it for a while. I'm too bloody old, I don't really enjoy it as much as I thought I would and now your mother's gone off her rocker and started asking for a divorce, I just thought "Fuck it, what's the point?"'

'Have you told her?'

'I sort of mentioned it this morning, but we haven't talked properly. I just wanted her to know before she went off to Margate to run me down with her mate. I thought it might shut her up. She's got a bloody cheek, going without me. And I tell you another thing, if she doesn't buck her ideas up now she's got her own way, I mean it, I'll pack my bags. See how she likes it on her own. She wouldn't last five minutes. No bloody money in flowers, is there?'

Steven allowed himself a little smile at his father's bluster when a flashing light in the rear-view mirror caught his eye. He slapped his dad's leg. 'Here you go, they're here.'

Rita's palm was sweaty around the top of her green plastic Marks & Spencer's bag and her shoes were beginning to pinch as she approached the club. She waited at the door for as long as it took to take a few deep breaths, then rang the bell. Frank's voice answered on the intercom immediately.

'It's me,' Rita said.

'Rita? What are you doing here?'

'I've been trying to get hold of you all morning. Let me in.'

The door buzzed and Rita went through, closing it behind her. The three men in the Granada looked at one another as she went in.

Rita stood in the dim of the upstairs bar and heard Frank's steps coming up from the office below. He looked slightly annoyed when he reached the bar.

'What's up? What are you doing here?'

'I didn't know how else to reach you.' Rita's rehearsed speech was put on hold as her eyes grew accustomed to the dark and she could see his face properly. 'What's wrong? You look like you've seen a ghost.'

Frank sighed. 'Nothing. I'm expecting somebody, that's all. Don't hang around up here, come down to the office.'

Rita had never been downstairs in the club and was shocked by the size of the 'office' – more of a storage cupboard with a desk, a two-door filing cabinet, a safe and a chair.

'You shouldn't have come here, Rita. And where's your husband? He was supposed to be here at twelve, it's quarter to three now.'

'I've come to tell you that I can't go to Margate with you. Ronnie turned up this morning back from Spain, I wasn't expecting him. I can't just go off and leave him . . . What do you mean Douggie hasn't turned up yet?' Rita went hot and cold.

He was about to speak when they could hear keys in the door upstairs. 'That'll be him now.' Frank sounded relieved.

Rita's mind raced. 'Oh my God, what am I going to say to him?'

'You don't say nothing, just stay there.' Frank closed the office door behind him and took the stairs two at a time to head Douggie off at the pass. He could hear whistling and the jangling of keys. But when he reached the top, it was Gully standing there looking pissed off.

'Oh well, if I knew you were going to be here I wouldn't have bothered. I'm supposed to be off Saturday afternoons.'

'What are you doing here? And where's Douggie?'

As Gully went into a long explanation about back axles and Billy Gaines, Rita started looking around the office. There wasn't much worth looking at – a couple of stock sheets, the rota – but she tucked her feet under the desk and had a good nose through anyway. When her feet came to rest on something soft, she pushed her chair back and looked under the desk, where she saw the holdall. Frank's weekend bag. It must be what he'd packed for Margate. Rita wondered what he'd been planning on wearing and slowly pulled back the zip. In her surprise she stood back and leaned against the door, where something sharp and heavy stuck in her back.

Upstairs, Frank was urging Gully to leave. 'You might as well push off, mate, I'll wait for Douggie.'

'What, I come all this way and don't even get a drink? Come on, Frank, sort me out, just a beer.'

'Look I'm expecting somebody, all right? Get yourself a fucking beer out of the fridge and drink up. I want you out of here in five minutes.' He looked at the front door, which was slightly ajar, and said, 'And don't forget to close that door behind you when you leave.' Frank turned impatiently and ran back down the stairs.

Outside, the three men in the Granada nodded at one another and stepped out of the car.

Frank found Rita sitting calmly at the desk tidying the pens.

'It's all right, it's Gully. Apparently Douggie broke down and he's waiting somewhere on the M3 for another van.'

'Gully?'

'Yeah, Douggie rang him and asked him to come up and let the builders in. He'll be gone in five minutes, you'd better go yourself as soon as he has.'

Then came a sound, the like of which she'd never heard before. Each shot had an echo that seemed to go on and on, a deep bass that made the walls vibrate. She'd only ever heard gunshots on the telly and hadn't imagined they could ever be so loud. Frank reached for his jacket hanging on the back of the door. He felt the lightness and looked at her. 'Where is it?'

'Where's what?' Rita swallowed hard.

'My gun, you stupid cow!' Frank grabbed her handbag and emptied the contents on the floor. Only lipsticks, a purse and some keys tumbled out. He shook her roughly. 'Where the fuck is it?' Rita stood up and started screaming. He threw her against the wall and ran up the stairs.

The door to the club was wide open, but Gully was alone in the bar. On his face was the strangest expression, a kind of puzzlement as if his last moments had been spent trying to get a joke he didn't understand.

Calmly, Frank closed the front door before studying Gully's slumped body: his head was resting on the footrail and there was a bloody mess where his torso had been. Only a sawn-off shotgun at close range could have made a hole that big. Rita climbed the stairs without a sound and crouched on about the fourth step from where she could spy Frank with his back to her gazing down at the corpse. She could see only Gully's boots, his feet at right angles. She didn't need to see the rest to work out what had happened.

'Call the police.' The steadiness in her voice surprised her. Frank turned and saw her pointing the gun at him.

'Put it down, Rita, you'll hurt yourself.' If he was nervous, it didn't show.

'Just do it, Frank.'

Frank walked towards her, his hand outstretched to take the gun, stopping about six feet short when she stood up and pointed the gun straight at his face. 'Rita, your old man is on his way to this club with a couple of hundred thousand pounds' worth of cocaine strapped to the back of his van that he doesn't even know about.'

'Don't lie to me, you can't put drugs in marble, it's solid.'

'You can if you hollow it out first. Now stop being a silly girl and give me the gun. Go home and I'll call you later when I've sorted this out.' He took a step forward.

'Sorted it out? He's lying there dead and you're going to sort it out? That could have been Douggie. Isn't it enough that you've set him up?'

Frank held up his hands in supplication. 'I did not set him up. Nothing's going to happen to Douggie, he doesn't know anything about it.'

'You're not bothered about me at all, are you? All this has been about keeping me sweet so you can get to Douggie.'

'That's not true, Rita, you know how I feel about you. I'll take care of you. It's not too late for us. We can go and live abroad. Just go home and forget you ever saw this.'

Rita's mouth hung open for several seconds until it caught up with her whirling mind. 'But Douggie. What about Douggie? Why did you get him involved? You've never been able to do your own dirty work, have you, Frank?'

'I didn't mean to involve Douggie. It got complicated, that's all. You don't know what you're talking about – now stop sodding around and give me that gun.'

Frank was getting short and when Rita screamed at him, 'Liar!', exasperated he turned away from her and walked behind the bar where he opened a bottle of Scotch. It was the way he sauntered off so nonchalantly and poured himself a drink that made her do it. Like he didn't take her seriously and there wasn't a dead body on the other side of the bar.

'You bastard.'

CHAPTER FIFTEEN

Love the One You're With

In the days and weeks following that fateful Saturday, Rita's family regarded her with a quiet awe. Even Douggie, his pride hurt that his wife had stepped in and taken care of a situation that, strictly speaking, she should have left to him, had to admit that he'd underestimated her. Nothing she'd done in twenty-six years of marriage could have made him think that she was capable of taking a pop at anybody. Although Rita had made the children promise to keep quiet – 'It's not the sort of thing you go around broadcasting' – Ronnie especially was beside himself with reflected glory and unable to wait for the new term to start; he had to call up all his schoolmates and tell them the incredible news. His friends were as full of praise as sixteen- and seventeen-year-olds ever allow themselves to be: 'Yeah, she's all right, your mum.'

Rita found it difficult to recall the exact sequence of events. She always prefaced the story with, 'All I can remember is feeling very angry and very hot, you know, like my head was going to explode.' The sight of his backside sticking up in the air, like he didn't have a care in the world, let alone a woman with a gun behind him, put Rita in a state beyond fury. She pointed wildly and pulled the trigger. Privately, it was his indifference to her and her wishes that had finally tipped the balance.

Frank had fallen forwards on to the floor behind the bar, his backside bleeding heavily. The bullet had passed through his left buttock and out the other side. The police later said it was the perfect shot for immobilising your enemy but keeping him alive – you could practise for years and not perfect that kind of shot.

As Frank lay on the floor with his hand pressed against his bloody cheek and a look of disbelief on his face, Rita had called out, 'Oh, are you all right?', as if she'd just spilt some hot tea down his trousers. He'd looked at her full of fury and screamed, 'Help me, I can't get up!' Rita looked at the gun in her hand and extended her arm so that it was as far away as possible from her, balanced on one finger through the trigger.

She felt very calm after that, as though the immediate danger had passed, and kept repeating to herself softly, 'Come on Douggie, come on Douggie', like a mantra. She couldn't look at Gully, and hid herself away downstairs. Above the phone in the office was a list of useful numbers: suppliers, the alarm company, members of staff and the direct line for the West End Central branch of the Metropolitan Police.

She dialled and spoke slowly to the receptionist: 'Hello, my name is Rita Fisher, I'm in the Poland Club. There's a man here who's been killed and I've just shot somebody. He's all right, I think, it's just his bum, but I think you should come with an ambulance.' She put the phone down, looked at the money in the holdall and wondered briefly about taking just a little; she decided that she was in enough trouble. The police were there within three minutes.

Rita spoke to the policemen as an ambulance crew lifted the groaning Frank on to a stretcher. His agony had more to do with Rita's uninterrupted flow of confession than with the wound to his backside.

'My husband should be here soon. He' – she pointed disgustedly to Frank's prone figure – 'says that the van is full of drugs and that my husband doesn't know anything about it. He wouldn't touch drugs, my Douggie, he thinks he's picking up a load of marble to do this place up.'

The investigating officer, who at first sight thought Rita a complete madwoman, slowly began to give credence to her story. It was too incredible not to be true. The only lie she told was about her reason for being at the scene of the crime in the first place: 'I was in town looking around the summer sales. I'd already been to Marks and thought I'd come by and see if my husband was about.'

She didn't think Douggie's pride would survive the truth.

Rita was disbelieving when Douggie and Steve were arrested and charged with possession with intent to supply and spent seven days on remand in Pentonville. She pleaded with the police: 'Look, I've told you the truth, I don't understand.' Finally they were released and all charges dropped when Frank did a bit of plea-bargaining.

Frank Skinner could afford the best brief money could buy and the appearance of a top QC at the police station did much to oil the negotiations. With a little co-operation, Frank faced seven years in an open prison at worst. His problems would begin in earnest when he got out. Collins's firm would certainly want to settle up. Rita was released without charge: she'd managed to do something that the police had been trying to do for years – pin down Frank Skinner. Unless Frank wanted to press charges for grievous assault, as far as the police were concerned, she was free to go.

Aside from his relatively recent drug trafficking, Frank's import/export activities – mostly pornographic – were of considerable interest to the investigating officers at West End Central. Matters were complicated by the fact that Frank had transferred the lease and all property connected with the club into Douggie's name. Customs and Excise would not get off Douggie's back so quickly.

Douggie was released just in time for Gully's funeral. Tania Gull had been inconsolable, unable to even think about arrangements, and was grateful to Rita for taking matters in hand. Rita had Tania stay at the house while Douggie and Steve were on remand. Rita did all the flowers for the ceremony at South London Crematorium. She'd done straightforward wreaths from the kids and as a special tribute from Tania had fashioned a dartboard using her best stock. The bull's-eye was a red rose with three darts feathering outwards from it. The floral dartboard took pride of place on top of the coffin inside the crematorium and accompanied Gully on his final journey from the chapel along the slow-moving conveyor belt to the oven beyond the curtains.

Nobody could go to work because all assets had been frozen until Customs and Excise completed their investigations. Car showrooms and florists were common fronts for money-laundering, but detailed investigation showed only minor discrepancies. Much to the surprise of the forces of law, the Fishers were practically straight. There would be minor charges against Douggie, but his brief was confident of a suspended sentence. For his part, Douggie was mourning not just the loss of his best friend, but also what he saw as his manhood. He had not only been duped wholesale by Frank Skinner and made to look a fool, but for his wife to have behaved in the way she did was to Douggie the equivalent of slicing off his testicles. 'I might as well start doing the bloody cooking as well.'

'Oh shut up, Douggie. What was I supposed to do?'

'I don't know what you were doing there in the first place.'

'I told you, I came to look for you. When you weren't home by one o'clock I started to get worried.' She knew that Douggie knew her story was full of holes. Rita never went into the West End if she could help it and she certainly never worried if he was a couple of hours late. All he could say was, 'At least we're all in one piece.'

Although they remained under the same roof, the cracks in their marriage widened for a few months. They were unable even to go to work to get away from one another.

Rita's shop was the first to be released from the powers of Customs and Excise and by the end of the summer the showroom was in business once more. But it was impossible to recapture the rhythm of their former lives. Their children hovered anxiously on the sidelines not knowing whether they'd be more help being around or staying well away. Douggie and Rita's fragile relationship looked at times as if it might break for ever. What should have brought them closer together looked for a while as if it might tear them apart. It was the shock of unexpected news that finally forced them to sit up and value what they had.

Doreen Skinner took her life with the help of around seventy tranquillisers on Bonfire Night. Douggie brought home the *Evening Standard* and they sat in the kitchen reading the small item over and over.

'She died of loneliness,' Rita said quietly.

'What do you mean?'

'Well, you wouldn't do that if you had people looking after you. Where were her bloody sons, I'd like to know?'

'You wouldn't ever do anything stupid, would you?' Douggie's eyes were glassy. Rita reached across the kitchen table and took his hands.

'Don't be silly, of course I wouldn't.'

'I couldn't stand it, Rita, I'd have to come with you.' She looked at him and knew that he meant it. Frank Skinner wouldn't have died for her.

'Come on, you.' Rita stood up and led him by the hand out of the kitchen and up the stairs. Peeping round the door of the front room, Ronnie saw their legs disappearing from view and turned to his sister to give her the thumbs-up.

'What's happening?' Marilyn whispered. Ronnie pointed upwards with his finger and said:

'Result.'